Topz SECRET Holiday DIARY

D0581569

Alexa Tewkesbury

CWR

Hi! We're the Topz Gang

Topz because we all live at the 'top' of something … either in houses at the top of the hill, at the top of the flats by the park, even sleeping in a top bunk counts! We are all Christians, and we go to Holly Hill School.

We love Jesus, and try to work out our faith in God in everything we do – at home, at school and with our friends. That even means trying to show God's love to the Dixons Gang, who tend to be bullies and can be a real pain!

If you'd like to know more about us, visit our website at **www.cwr.org.uk/topz** You can read all about us, and how you can get to know and understand the Bible more by reading our *Topz* notes, which are great fun, and written every two months just for you!

Holidiary

My name begins with:

_____

and ends with:

_____

and that's all I'm saying!
(After all, this is my Topz SECRET Holidiary!)

**Here is a picture of me on holiday with
one of my best friends**

(Draw a picture of yourself and a friend on
holiday here, whether you've been on holiday
together or not.)

Why Holidays are Topz!

However much you like school (and especially if you don't like it!), holidays are TOPZ!

Whatever the time of year, you can't beat having some space to do a bit of what you want, when you want.

Weekends are cool ... but holidays are AWESOME! Here are my five favourite things about being on holiday:

John's fave five
- No getting up early to get to school.
- No wearing school uniform.
- No homework! Whoop!
- No teachers telling you what to do all day long.
- No having to queue up for lunch.

Hmmm ... I don't think John likes school very much, do you?

There are tons of reasons why holidays are stonking – not just because there's no school.

You've read John's fave five things about holidays. Now see if you can come up with a fave five of your own.

Your fave five things about being on holiday

1.

2.

3.

4.

5.

Are any of your fave five the same as John's?

Holiday Treats!

Here's a list of popular places to go and cool things to do for an extra-special holiday day:

Cinema	Museum	Ice skating
Cycling	Seaside	Horse riding
Quad biking	Zoo	Swimming
Fair	Theme park	Skateboarding

Can you find them all in the word search?

```
Z  C  A  S  W  I  M  M  I  N  G  J  V  F  R
K  Y  J  A  R  K  R  A  P  E  M  E  H  T  M
U  C  J  R  M  N  E  D  P  A  N  G  L  M  X
R  L  U  I  C  E  S  K  A  T  I  N  G  M  J
E  I  F  Y  I  K  V  E  Z  A  S  I  I  C  Z
T  N  A  J  A  G  N  I  K  I  B  D  A  U  Q
A  G  W  F  C  O  V  C  M  Z  Z  R  O  E  E
I  N  O  O  E  I  Y  S  B  U  V  A  M  E  K
G  N  I  D  I  R  E  S  R  O  H  O  U  U  K
E  R  D  T  I  A  N  E  Y  A  C  B  E  A  H
F  L  S  Q  S  B  O  O  Z  I  Y  E  S  L  F
K  O  B  I  I  D  N  L  N  B  I  T  U  S  A
J  A  D  B  C  Q  U  E  E  N  H  A  M  S  I
N  E  Q  E  I  U  M  K  M  G  B  K  J  Z  R
V  G  F  X  A  A  W  U  A  E  R  S  Z  B  P
```

Answer on page 120

If you could choose to do anything on this list today, what would it be?

_____

Topz Holiday Fun Facts

Did you know ...?

- In Victorian times (when Queen Victoria was on the throne of England) more and more people began to go by train to the seaside for their holidays.
- People who could afford to stay at the seaside might go on holiday for a week or so. Some would go just for the day.
- Seaside places like Blackpool and Brighton grew to be firm favourites for the Victorians.
- There was seaside entertainment for Victorian holiday-makers, including *Punch and Judy* puppet shows.
- Some Victorians didn't own a swimming costume, so they had to hire one!
- On beaches there were wooden huts on wheels called bathing machines. Inside these, the Victorians could change into their costumes in private. Then the bathing machine was pulled down to the edge of the sea so that the people inside could hop straight into the waves. They didn't think anyone should see them walking around in a swimming costume!

Josie's Happy Holidiary

Tuesday, 4pm

Seriously FANDABULOUS news!

Gabby just rang:

Gabby: Hey, Josie, it's Gabby.

Me: Hi, Gabby. What's up?

Gabby: Something very cool. Shall I tell you straightaway or do you want a bit of time to enjoy the fact that I have something unbelievably awesome to tell you? Well, to ask you?

Me: Oooh, I don't know!

Gabby: Guess what it is.

Me: I can't! I don't have a clue.

Gabby: Erm … that's why it's called a 'guess'.

Me: OK, er … you're moving to Holly Hill.

Gabby: No. I mean that's not very likely, is it?

Me: S'pose not. Would be unbelievably awesome, though.

Gabby: True. Guess again.

Me: Erm … You're getting a horse?

Gabby: Nope.

Me: Erm … You're getting a horse and giving it to me?

Gabby: I don't think you're taking this very seriously.

Me: Gabby, honestly, I have absolutely no idea. Just tell me!

Gabby: Well …

Me: Yes?

Gabby: Well, you know it's my birthday next Wednesday?

Me: Yes, of course.

Gabby: Well, you know Chrissie and Rich are taking

me to London with my friend, Sabita, from school and we're going to go to Hamleys, that big toyshop, and then to the theatre?

Me: How could I forget? Sounds like the best birthday treat ever! Not to mention the best holiday day you are probably going to have this whole school holiday!

Gabby: Yes, exactly. Well, the not-so-awesome bit is that Sabita can't come now. She's really disappointed so we're going to bring her back something brilliant from Hamleys to make up for it. But ...

Me: Yes?

Gabby: Well ...

Me: Yes?

Gabby: Are you ready for me to tell you the unbelievably awesome bit now?

Me: YES!!

Gabby: OK then ... I'd like to invite you instead.

Me: Wahooo! Whoop whoop and whoopitty whoop!

Gabby: You'd like to come with us then?

Me: Would I like to come with you? WOULD I LIKE TO COME WITH YOU? YESSS!!

See? **Seriously** FANDABULOUS! Wait till I tell Sarah!

Tuesday, 4.30pm

You see, some things are fandabulous and some things *should be* fandabulous. And this – going to London with Gabby and Auntie Chrissie and Uncle Rich for Gabby's birthday – should be one of the most fandabulous things ever.

But nothing's ever that simple, is it?

Why can't things just be simple?

Tuesday, 4.45pm

I said to Mum, 'Guess what? Gabby's friend, Sabita, can't go to London with her and Auntie Chrissie and Uncle Rich for Gabby's birthday treat now. So Gabby's invited ME to go instead! We're going to Hamleys and to the theatre! I reckon Auntie Chrissie and Uncle Rich must be just about the best foster parents in the whole world. I'm so glad they found Gabby. Not just because I get to join in her fantastic birthday, but because they love Gabby so much. They really do! And what she really needed was people to love her. I *can* go, can't I, Mum? To London, I mean? We're going to have totally the best time!'

'I'm sure you can go, sweetheart,' Mum smiled. 'When is it?'

'Next Wednesday.'

'Sounds fine to me. How exciting for you!'

'I know!' I said. 'Wait till I tell Sarah!'

That's when Mum said, 'Oh ...'

'What?' I asked.

'Next Wednesday ...' Mum murmured. 'You're sure it's next Wednesday?'

'Of course I'm sure. Completely and utterly positive. Why?'

'It's just that next Wednesday ... Well, isn't that ...?'

'*What?* '

'Well, isn't that when you're supposed to be having a girly day with Sarah – because John's off with Danny and Benny doing that special football training thing, which Greg's arranged for youth club?'

My heart fell into my boots. (I've read that in books before and never really known what it meant – until now.)

'No! Nooo!'

'Don't panic,' Mum said. 'I might have got that

wrong. The girly day could be a different Wednesday.'

'It's not a girly day,' I murmured. 'It's a "girls only" day.'

Mum was already looking at the calendar.

There was no need.

She hadn't got it wrong. She'd got it horribly, HORRIFICALLY RIGHT.

Sarah has this 'girls only' day all planned out. She's even got a haircut booked and I'm going to sit with her while she has it done. And we're going to look through the hairstyle magazines and all the different bottles and pots of stuff on the shelves at the hairdresser's that you can put on your hair to give it a 'dazzling shine' or 'intense volume' (whatever that is). And we're going to have ice cream afterwards at the café and then we're going to the shopping centre. And it's all going to be great and cool and snazzy, like everything is that Sarah and I do together.

Only, I'd forgotten.

I'd forgotten it was next Wednesday.

Gabby invited me to have the best day in the world in London for her birthday – and I forgot all about Sarah.

Tuesday, 7pm

Mum says, 'This is so silly, you know, Josie. All you have to do is have a chat with Sarah about it. Tell her how much it would mean to you *and* to Gabby if you could go to London next Wednesday. Say that you're very, very sorry the days have clashed, but to make up for it, you'll have two girly days with her instead. Or three if she wants. After all, it is the holidays.'

'"Girls only",' I muttered. 'They're not girly days, they're "girls only" days.'

'Isn't it the same thing?' Mum asked.

13

'Well, no, obviously,' I answered.

'Just chat to her, Josie,' Mum said. 'I'm sure Sarah will understand.'

Tuesday, 7.15pm

You see, I'm not. I'm not sure Sarah will understand at all. She's my best friend in the whole wide world and she always will be. But the 'girls only' day has been arranged for about the last three weeks and Sarah simply will not understand if I say I want to go to London with Gabby instead.

She simply will not.

Tuesday, 7.30pm

How can this have happened?

7.35pm

How, how, how?

7.40pm

Just tell me HOW??

Wednesday, 6am

What will I be doing exactly this time next week? Getting ready for Sarah's 'girls only' day, or getting ready to go to London?

Wednesday, 8am

Mum said, 'Have you spoken to Sarah yet?'

I said, 'No.'

Mum said, 'You know, the sooner you do it, the more you can get on and enjoy your holiday.'

'I know,' I said.

The problem is, what to say to Sarah …? What to say …?

Wednesday, 9am
Oh genius, genius! I must be (probably) the ultimate
genius!

I've worked it out – what I'm going to say. How I'm
going to tell Sarah about next Wednesday!

I'm not actually going to say anything about it at all!
How genius is that! I'm going to carry on as though the
'girls only' day is still happening. Then the day before
– on the Tuesday – I'm going to start not to feel well!
I won't really be not feeling well obviously – at least
I hope I won't be otherwise I won't be able to go to
London! I'll just pretend. I'll say I have to stay in bed
because of a sore throat. Tonsillitis maybe. I had that
once. So did Sarah and it was horrid.

So then Sarah will have to understand why I can't
possibly have a day out. I mean I *will* be having a day
out – with Gabby. But Sarah won't know that. She'll
think I'm ill in bed so she won't even be upset. She'll just
feel sorry that I'm not well.

Ha ha! I just am *such* a genius!!

Wednesday, 10am
I must be the worst friend in the whole world.

I said to Mum, 'You'll tell Sarah I'm ill, won't you, Mum?
Then she won't have to know I'm going off with Gabby
instead of with her. And then she won't get upset.'

Mum looked at me. She stopped what she was doing
and just looked at me.

'No, Josie,' she said. 'No, I most certainly will not.'

'Why not?' I demanded.

'Because it's a lie. Isn't it?'

I could feel my cheeks going hot. Red.

'Sarah's your best friend. Your very best friend,' Mum said. 'And I don't tell lies, Josie. So I'm certainly not going to start now.'

Wednesday, 11am

Mum says we all get tempted to do wrong things sometimes. Things that God doesn't want us to do. She says *she* does. And Dad does – although it's hard to think of Mum and Dad doing anything wrong ever.

But Mum says there's a difference between being *tempted* to do something wrong and *actually* doing something wrong. She says that if we're tempted to do something that God won't like, then we can ask God to help us – *really* help us – not to do it. Being tempted means having a wrong thought or idea. And we can't seem to help having those. But we only actually *do wrong* if we go ahead and do the thing God doesn't want us to do.

'You've thought about telling a lie,' Mum said. 'You thought that if you did that, Sarah wouldn't get upset and you could get what you want – a trip to London with Gabby. But then *I* have to tell the lie, too, don't I? So does Dad. *And* Gabby probably, because she's bound to talk to Sarah some time soon. So a little lie gets bigger and bigger. We all end up doing the wrong thing. That's not what God wants, Josie.'

'I'm the worst friend in the world,' I said. 'And God must think I'm horrible.'

'No,' laughed Mum. 'God loves you! You've been tempted – yes. Like I say, we all get tempted. God knows that and He understands. So ask Him to help you stand up to that temptation. And He will. Then go and ring Sarah and explain that Gabby's asked you to go to London with her because her friend can't. Tell her the truth.'

Wednesday, 1pm
Sarah's very cool. Probably the coolest best friend anyone could have.

'Hi, Sarah,' I said. 'Would you be really upset if we changed next Wednesday to a different day?'

'Why?' Sarah asked.

'Because it's Gabby's birthday and she *was* going to London next Wednesday with her friend, Sabita, and Auntie Chrissie and Uncle Rich. Only now Sabita can't go. So she's asked me to go with her instead. And of course I won't if you really don't want me to. I just wondered if we could maybe have our "girls only" day on a day that isn't next Wednesday.'

'Oh,' Sarah sighed. 'I wanted it to be next Wednesday because John's going off with Benny and Danny.'

'I know.'

'And Mum's already booked my haircut.'

'I know.'

'And I was really looking forward to it.'

'I know.'

'Well ... I'd still better go and have my hair cut,' Sarah said slowly. 'But you don't really need to be there for that. Mum'll come with me. And we could always have ice cream and do shopping another day. Thursday would be good. Then John will be doing his thing one day, and we'll be doing ours the next. And Gabby will probably be sad if you can't go to London ... So let's have our "girls only" day on Thursday. OK?'

Wednesday night. In bed

Mum just showed me a bit in the Bible.

'This is just for you,' she said.

It's from Philippians chapter 4, verses 8 to 9: *'fill your minds with those things that are good and that deserve praise: things that are true, noble, right, pure, lovely, and honourable ... And the God who gives us peace will be with you.'*

'You did the right thing, Josie,' Mum said. 'Think how much happier next Wednesday will be because you did the right thing.'

Benny's Barmy Beach Hut

I LOVE holiday days at the seaside! Our family has a beach hut. It's so cool! We keep a camping stove and a kettle in it, so Mum and Dad can make a cup of tea. We also have a cricket set in there, so we can all play cricket (obviously). We've got folding chairs, books and magazines, and spare towels and stuff in the summer. And if the weather gets too hot or too cold, we can sit inside and watch the sea through the open door!

Sarah and John's beach hut is stonking! But if I could have one of my very own, here's what I'd keep in it:

- a MASSIVE tin of chocolate biscuits
- lots of BIG bottles of lemonade
- a football
- a skateboard
- a bike
- some board games
- a HUGE jigsaw puzzle that would take AGES to do so that I could keep adding pieces each time I went to the seaside
- an emergency supply of crisps
- spare jeans and jumper (for when I accidentally fall over in the sea (which I do quite often) when I go paddling in winter)

More Beach Hut Barminess

If Benny ever has a beach hut, he wants it to look like this:

If you ever had a beach hut of your own, what would you want it to look like? Draw it here:

What would you keep in your beach hut?

_____

_____

_____

_____

Which of your friends would you most like to visit your beach hut with you on a day at the seaside?

_____

Which famous person would you most like to visit your beach hut with you?

_____

Which member of the Topz Gang would you most like to visit your beach hut with you?

_____

Spot the Difference!

These five beach huts are all exactly the same – except for one. Can you spot which one it is?

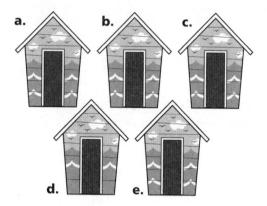

a.   b.   c.

d.   e.

Answer on page 120

Create your own 'spot the difference'. Use patterns to decorate these five beach huts. Four of them must be identical, with just one having a slight difference. When you've finished, show the huts to your family and friends to see if they can 'spot the difference'.

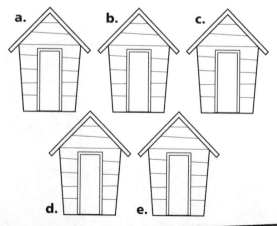

a.   b.   c.

d.   e.

Making Journeys

'Going away' for a holiday obviously means going on a journey. It might be a long journey or a short one. But now that flying in an aeroplane is so quick and easy, people can travel all over the world.

Flying from London, England, see if you can match the approximate hours it takes with the correct destination (a world map might help!):

1 hour	**New York**
3 hours	**Manchester**
5 hours	**Singapore**
7/8 hours	**Egypt**
13 hours	**Iceland**

Answers on page 120

If you've been away on holiday, what's the furthest place you've travelled to?

_____

How long did it take you to get there?

_____

Walk This Way!

Even before aeroplanes, people made long journeys. It just took them much longer. In fact, people have been making journeys for thousands of years.

The Bible mentions lots and lots of travellers – although the people it tells us about weren't travelling because they were going on holiday. Bible travellers must have been very fit people, too! Sometimes they might have ridden donkeys or camels, but a lot of the time, they would have walked.

How much do you walk? Answer these questions to find out:

Do you walk to school?	**yes/no**
Do you walk to the shops?	**yes/no**
Do you walk to your local park (if you have one)?	**yes/no**
Do you walk with a dog?	**yes/no**
Do you go for walks just for fun?	**yes/no**
Do you ENJOY a good walk?	**yes/no**

Look at your answers. If they are all 'no', perhaps it's time to grab your boots (and maybe a parent or carer!) and *get walking*!

Dave's Crazy Caravan Holidiary

Day One

I'm excited, but Dad's way more excited than I am. I'd go so far as to say he is way more excited than I have ever seen him.

The caravan he bought from Mr Crowden across the road has been standing on the drive for the last six weeks. Dad's been itching to get us all away for a family holiday in it.

And today's the day.

Mum's calling reminders through the kitchen window.

Mum: You've packed the sleeping bags, haven't you?
Dad: Yes.
Mum: Do you think you should check?
Dad: Why? I know I've packed them.
Mum: Just check for me, would you? It won't take a second.
Dad: But it's a second I don't need to take. The sleeping bags are in there. I know they are. I put them in there myself.
Mum: Well, I hope you're right because I don't want to be in the middle of a caravan park somewhere miles from home without a sleeping bag.

Pause.

Mum: You've put the flask in, haven't you?
Dad: Yes.
Mum: Definitely?
Dad: Definitely.
Mum: Because if there's one thing I need when I'm camping it's a continuous supply of hot coffee.
Dad: We're not camping. We're caravanning.
Mum: Same thing.
Dad: No, it is not! Camping is damp and cold and lying awake through the night on the hard ground. Caravanning is a whole new world of excitement, adventure and comfy beds.
Mum: Just check that you've packed the flask, would you?
Dad: No need. I've packed the flask. The flask – is packed.

It's been like that all morning.
   We were supposed to leave at 11 o'clock.
   Now Dad's aiming to set off after lunch.

After lunch
John texted.
   Have U gone yet?
   I texted, *Not yet no.*
   John texted, *Y not?*
   I texted, *Packing. Seems 2 B taking a long time.*
   John texted, *Y?*
   I texted, *Parents.*
   John texted, *OK. Understood.*

2.30pm
'So are we still going today or not?' asked Mum.
   'Of course we are,' replied Dad. He's been messing about with something at the front of the caravan for

ages. 'I'm just having a bit of trouble with the … with the, erm …'

'With the what?' asked Mum.

Dad replied, 'The erm … Well, I don't know what it's called but I'm having a bit of trouble with it.'

3pm

'If you ask me, it's getting a bit late to go now,' said Mum.

Dad was still having trouble.

'It's never too late,' he said. 'Let me go and ring Mr Crowden. He'll know what to do.'

He disappeared inside the house.

'Well?' said Mum when he came out again.

'No answer,' Dad said.

3.30pm

The thing about Dad is that he never gives up.

Never.

Not even when anyone else would have given up ages ago.

Not even when he probably should.

5pm

Dad called, 'We're all hitched up! Time to go!'

Mum said, 'Oh, we're not still going today, are we? It'll be dark by the time we get there.'

'Doesn't matter,' said Dad. 'Won't take long to set up once we're in the caravan park.'

'But it's silly,' said Mum. 'You don't even know where we're going.'

'Do we ever know where we're going when we go on holiday?' Dad replied. 'That's why we have a map.'

'Well, I won't be able to read a map once it's dark,'

said Mum.

'And that's why we have a torch,' said Dad.

5.15pm
John texted.
U must have gone by now.
Just, I texted.
John texted, *Seriously?*
I texted, *I am always serious.*

7.30pm
'Mum,' I said. 'Are we stopping soon? I'm getting really hungry.'

'So am I,' said Mum. 'You'd better ask your dad. He's the one with the steering wheel.'

'Dad,' I said. 'I'm getting really hungry.'

'Well,' Dad said, 'I reckon we should be there soon. Another couple of hours.'

'Erm, Dad,' I said, 'another couple of hours is not soon. And the thing is, I'm getting really hungry now.'

'So am I, Dave,' Dad said, 'so am I.'

9.30pm
Mum's holding the torch. Dad's looking at the map.

'I'm sure this is right,' Dad's saying. 'We came off that road, turned left there, followed it all the way to the junction.'

'Odd, isn't it?' grunted Mum. 'You've done all the right things and we still seem to have ended up in the wrong place.'

My stomach's grumbling. I think I will faint from hunger if I don't have something to eat soon.

9.35pm
John texted.
  R U there yet?
  No, I texted.
  Y not? John texted.
  We don't knw where we R, I texted.
We may B lost 4ever.
  That's bad, John texted.
  Yes, I texted. *And I'm starving.*

10pm
It wasn't really Dad's fault. He was only trying to turn
us around. It's just he's never driven backwards with a
caravan before. In the dark. Or in the daylight come to
think of it.

So now the caravan's stuck in a ditch and he can't get
the car to start.

But it really wasn't Dad's fault.

10.30pm
Dad got back in the car. He's just phoned the
breakdown people.

'Someone will be here soon,' he announced.
'How soon?' asked Mum.
I couldn't see her face. Partly because I was sitting
behind her. Partly because it was dark. But I could hear
it in her voice. She wasn't happy.
'Very soon,' said Dad.
'How soon – *exactly?*'
'About ... an hour and a half.'
'*What?*'
No. Mum wasn't happy at all.

11pm

I'm all right now. I've eaten a whole packet of biscuits. Most of our stuff's in the caravan, and Dad didn't want to go in there while it was in a ditch. But there was a small bag of food in the car boot, so we've been eating that.

I ate the biscuits.

Mum ate the fruit cake.

Dad ate the crisps and the celery.

11.15pm

'Sorry things haven't quite gone to plan,' Dad said.

'It's fine,' sighed Mum. 'I never thought for one minute they would.'

'I did,' said Dad. 'I was quite confident.'

'Now, why doesn't that surprise me?' said Mum.

11.30pm

Bright lights! Bright orange flashy lights!

The breakdown man's here!

Day Two

7am

Dad says you can either get all miserable and worked up about things, or you can learn to look on the bright side.

Last night Mum said, 'And where is the bright side here? The car's broken down, the caravan's stuck in a ditch, we've no idea where we are and it's the middle of the night.'

Dad said, 'Well, yes. I agree that sometimes the bright side is not so easy to find. But then again, look at us. We're all right, aren't we? We're not hurt. We're not even hungry any more. Are we, Dave? And any minute now,' he added 'we'll be rescued. You see the bright side is that this is all just part of our crazy caravan adventure.'

Dad looked at Mum and smiled. Mum smiled back.

Then, 'I tell you what, though,' Dad said. 'I'll swap you a stick of celery for a piece of fruitcake.'

7.25am

I admire my dad. The way he can do that. Always look on the bright side.

He says he didn't used to. He says he used to get really worried about things. So worried that he'd get bad headaches and make himself feel really ill.

But then one day he realised something. A HUGE something.

He realised that when things went wrong – that's when he had to trust God the most.

And the more he trusted God, the closer he felt to Him.

The more he felt God was really taking care of him.

And God's never let him down.

7.30am

John texted.

So how is it?

I texted, *How's wot?*

Ur crazy caravan adventure, John texted, *what do U think?*

Pretty crazy, I said. *We had 2 get rescued by a breakdown man.*

No way! texted John.

Yes way, I texted.

Where were U? John texted.

31

No idea, I texted. *We were lost at the time.*

Lost where?

If I knew that we wouldn't have been lost would we?

Good point.

I thought so.

John texted, *So where R U now?*

In bed, I texted.

Still? John texted. *Don't U wanna get out – start xploring?*

Not much 2 xplore really, I texted.

Wot do U mean? Must B dead exciting 2 B away in a caravan!

Must B, I texted. *Would B – if we were. But we're not.*

Wot?

Dad says we'll have a crazy caravan adventure some other time. We're back in Holly Hill.

More TOPZ Holiday Fun Facts!

- Going on holiday in caravans began right back in the 1880s. Of course, back then they would have been pulled by horses, not cars. The very first 'touring' caravan was called 'The Wanderer'. Good name!

- Hotels (or 'inns' as they used to be known) have been around for thousands of years. They are mentioned in the Bible – Mary and Joseph weren't able to stay in an inn on the very first Christmas because all the rooms were full. Over the years, as people have begun to travel more and more, hotels have sprung up all over the place. And these days, many of them give you fabulous things to do. Even if Mary and Joseph had found a room in Bethlehem, their inn probably wouldn't have had a swimming pool, beauty salon, sauna or gym!!

- The very first camping site (for tents) is thought to have opened in 1894 on the Isle of Man.

- The royal family in the UK owned a beach hut in Norfolk, England for 70 years. Sadly it burned down in a fire in 2003.

Have you ever been on holiday in …?

☐ a hotel   ☐ a caravan   ☐ a tent

(Tick more than one box if you need to.)

Bible Travellers

Have you heard of these famous journey-makers?

- **Jonah** travelled in the opposite direction God wanted him to go in – and ended up being swallowed by a huge fish! (Read his story in the book of Jonah in the Old Testament.)

- **Naomi** travelled with her husband and two sons to a different country because there was a terrible famine (no food) where they lived. When the famine was over, Naomi travelled back to her home country again, with her daughter-in-law, **Ruth**. (Read their story in the Old Testament in the book of Ruth.)

- **Hannah** and her husband, **Elkanah**, travelled once a year, every year, to a special place called Shiloh to worship God. (Read their story in the Old Testament in the book of 1 Samuel, chapter 1.)

- **Paul** travelled to lots of different places to teach people all about Jesus. (Read about him in the New Testament in the book of Acts. Paul also wrote letters to the people he visited on his travels or who had travelled with him. You can read them in the New Testament, too: Romans, Corinthians, Galatians, Ephesians, Philippians, Colossians, Thessalonians, Timothy, Titus and Philemon. That's a lot of letters – and a lot of journeys!)

- God's special people, the Israelites, also went on a long and difficult journey. God had a beautiful place ready for them, where He wanted them to live. The Bible calls it 'the promised land'. Two men travelled with the Israelites to lead them – first a man called **Moses** and then a man called **Joshua**. (Their stories are found in the Old Testament, starting in Exodus and ending in Joshua.)

But there are two travellers written about in the Bible who are perhaps more famous than all the others. Can you guess who they are? (BIG clue: You might hear about them every year around Christmas time!)

Their names were:

1. M _____ and J _____

And do you know …?

2. Where they were travelling from? _____

3. Where they were travelling to? _____

4. Why they were travelling? _____

5. Who else set off on a long journey to meet Jesus soon after He was born? (Tick the right answer)

☐ doctors   ☐ fishermen

☐ wise men   ☐ highwaymen

Answers on page 120

Josie's Rainy Day Quiz

Whatever time of year you're on holiday from school, there may very well be wet days (boo!). So, if you're stuck for something to do the next time it rains, try my quiz!

In which country would you find each of these famous landmarks? Write the answer underneath each one.

Eiffel Tower

_____

Nelson's Column

_____

Taj Mahal

_____

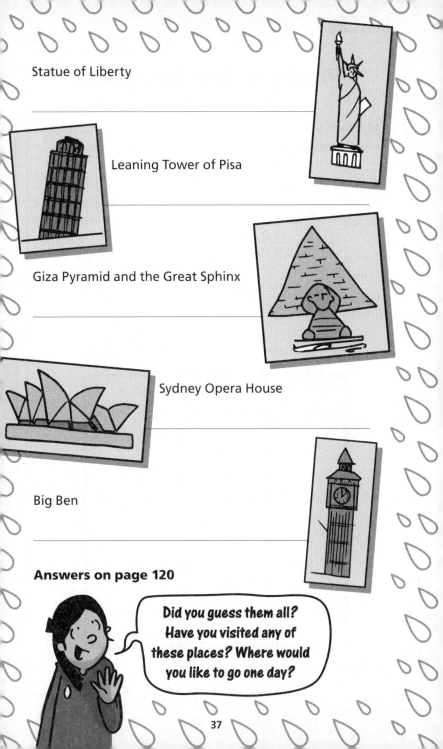

Statue of Liberty

Leaning Tower of Pisa

Giza Pyramid and the Great Sphinx

Sydney Opera House

Big Ben

Answers on page 120

Did you guess them all?
Have you visited any of
these places? Where would
you like to go one day?

37

What's in Your Suitcase?

Wherever you go on holiday, you'll have to pack a suitcase with all the things you might need while you're away.

Here are a few things you might want to remember to take with you (some things are for summer holidays, some are for winter holidays, and some are for both!):

Sun cream
Camera
Sunglasses
Gloves

Thick socks
Good book
Bible

Woolly hat
Swimsuit
Shampoo

Now see if you can spot them all in the word search:

O	Q	S	G	O	O	D	B	O	O	K	N
W	S	J	H	H	N	J	S	P	Y	S	S
O	Z	E	R	A	V	J	Q	H	K	K	W
O	G	U	S	B	M	T	T	C	G	T	I
L	L	A	O	S	P	P	O	F	Y	P	M
L	O	Q	B	D	A	S	O	U	U	S	S
Y	V	F	Q	I	K	L	L	O	R	C	U
H	E	G	I	C	B	X	G	U	T	M	I
A	S	U	I	J	B	L	X	N	H	I	T
T	M	H	E	A	K	K	E	T	U	M	F
L	T	S	U	N	C	R	E	A	M	S	Z
E	A	R	E	M	A	C	J	Q	E	B	R

Answer on page 121

Danny's Desperate Holidiary

Tuesday

'Paul,' I said. 'Really need your help.'

'Cool,' Paul said. 'To do what?'

'Run the Holly Hill mini-marathon.'

Paul looked doubtful. 'You want *me* to help you run a marathon?'

'A *mini*-marathon. Yeah.'

'Erm … OK,' Paul said. 'I mean, I've never run a marathon before, but how hard can it be?'

'No, no, you don't understand,' I said. 'You're not going to run the marathon, *I* am. *You're* gonna help me train.'

'Oh, right!' grinned Paul. 'That's a relief. I'm not sure I'm built for marathon-running. I think I need to wait until my legs grow a bit longer. Assuming they're going to grow longer, that is. But … are you sure you want me? I wouldn't know how to train *myself* let alone anyone else.'

'Doesn't matter,' said Danny. 'I'll tell you everything I want you to do. Mostly it's moral support. And you're ace at that.'

'Awesome,' Paul nodded. 'I was wondering what I was going to do this holiday. So – Paul, the personal trainer, huh? I like the sound of that.'

'Yeah. Oh, and Paul?'

'What?'

'You're going to need your bike.'

Wednesday

'What are you doing today?' Mum asked.

'Training,' I said. 'I want to be fastest in the

39

Holly Hill mini-marathon. I want my name on the trophy.'

'Do you now?' Mum said.

'I can do it, I know I can,' I said. 'And I've got two weeks to get ready.'

Dad shook his head. 'Two weeks? Doesn't sound very long to me.'

'It's loads of time,' I said. 'It's only a *mini*-marathon.'

'I doubt I could get ready for a mini-marathon in two weeks,' grunted Dad.

'Er, no offence, Dad – but I mean, you are a bit ... well ... old.'

'Your father is not old,' said Mum. 'And he's actually extremely sprightly ... for his age. You've seen him down on the allotment. If there was a prize for digging potatoes, I'm sure he'd win it.'

'Like I say, no offence,' I said. 'It's just that I know I can run and I know Dad can't. Not without a lot of training. Not fast. Can you, Dad?'

'Not fast perhaps,' Dad agreed, 'but the potato thing is very true. If we went head-to-head potato-digging, you wouldn't stand a chance.'

Evening

Two hours' training this afternoon. Followed by a long soak in the bath.

I told Paul he ought to soak in a bath, too.

'Why? Do I smell?' Paul asked.

'No. Well, maybe a bit. But that's because I've been running and you've been cycling along behind me. It's hot work cycling. And soaking in a bath is meant to be good for your muscles after exercise.'

I got Paul to time my running, too. Doing laps of the park – two at a time.

I gave him the stopwatch and said, 'Tell me when to go.'

'Ready, steady, GO!' yelled Paul.

I did my first two laps. It wasn't even hard.

When I got back to Paul, I said, 'How long?'

'How long until what?' Paul answered.

'How long did it take me to do the two laps?'

'Erm … well, not long,' Paul said. 'Actually I think you were pretty quick.'

'Yes, but *how* long? What does the stopwatch say?'

Paul looked down at it. 'Oh. Was I supposed to switch it on?'

'Well, yeah! That's how you know how long it's taking me. That's how you can see if I'm getting better.'

'Right!' nodded Paul. 'Now I get it! Erm … and how do I switch it on, exactly?'

Thursday

'Off again?' said Mum.

'Yup,' I said.

'You won't overdo it, will you?' Mum said. 'It is only a *mini*-marathon.'

'Yes, Mum,' I said, 'but it's a mini-marathon I'm going to win. And this is just the start. Afterwards, who knows? One day I want to run in the London Marathon. And not just run in it. I want to be the fastest!'

'You're so competitive, Danny,' said Mum. 'I wonder where you get it from?'

'That'll be from me,' said Dad. 'This year I am definitely entering the 'Biggest Cauliflower' contest in the Holly Hill Garden Show. And nothing is going to stop me.'

Sunday

After Sunday Club, Paul said, 'Are we training today? Or are we having a day off – as it's Sunday?'

'We can't have a day off,' I said. 'We've got to keep it up. That's what you do if you're serious about something. You keep it up.'

We were helping Greg to stack chairs in the church hall.

'I've heard all about your training,' Greg said. 'You're the coach, are you, Paul?'

'Well, sort of,' Paul said. 'I'm the personal trainer.'

'Ooh, very posh,' said Greg.

'Although, to be honest,' said Paul, 'I'm not sure you really need me, Danny. I mean, I'm supposed to be the one cycling behind you and telling *you* to keep going and not to stop. But half the time it's you turning round to me while you're running and telling me to keep up!'

'I *do* need you, Paul,' I said. 'I need you heaps. If I was doing this on my own, I might have given up by now.'

'I don't think you would have done,' said Paul. 'You want your name on that trophy too much.'

'Oh, there's a trophy, is there?' said Greg.

'Yeah!' I answered. 'This is serious business, Greg. I want to be a champion marathon runner. And it starts right here. Right now.'

Tuesday

One week down, one to go.

I just hope I'm getting fast enough. I've got to be fast enough!

Friday

'Paul,' I said. 'Where are you?'

I had to hold my mobile inside my hood. It was

throwing it down with rain.

'I'm at home,' said Paul. 'In the dry.'

'Why?' I asked. 'I'm waiting for you at the park.'

'Really?' said Paul. 'But it's pouring. I mean *really* pouring. It's like bucketfuls coming down outside my window.'

'So?' I said.

'So,' said Paul, 'we'll get soaked.'

'And what about on mini-marathon day?' I said. 'What if it's raining then? Am I *not* going to run because I'll get wet? Am I supposed to think, "That's a pain, it's raining. Oh well, maybe I won't bother"? Well, am I?'

'Well, I think *I* might.'

'Yes, Paul, but you're not me, are you? You don't care about being fastest in the mini-marathon.'

'Erm, Danny?' Paul said. 'You don't think maybe you're taking this a little bit too seriously, do you? I know it'd be great to be fastest but … does it really matter that much?'

Does it really matter that much? What sort of attitude's that for a personal trainer?

'Yes, Paul,' I said. 'It does matter that much. At least it does to me. Oh, forget about it. I'll do it on my own.'

I still thought he might come to the park.

He didn't.

In bed

We've just had a games night at youth group. Greg even put out the table tennis. He hasn't done that for ages.

'You've probably been cooped up indoors all day with the weather like this,' he said. 'I thought you could do with burning off some energy.'

'I've burnt off lots of energy already,' I said.

'You didn't go running in the pouring rain, did you?' Greg asked.

'Yup,' I said. 'But my personal trainer bottled out.'

'I didn't want to get wet,' Paul shrugged. 'Well, not *that* wet.'

'Fair enough if you ask me,' said Greg.

'You see, that's the difference between being competitive, and *not* being competitive,' I said. 'Right now, I want my name on that trophy more than I want anything else in the whole world.'

Saturday

Three days till mini-marathon day.

After training, Paul said, 'You must have run miles, Danny. Miles and miles since you started getting ready for this marathon. And I must have cycled quite a lot of miles, too. If I had a job as a personal trainer, I'd get really fit, wouldn't I?'

I said, 'Yes. But you'd have to get over your fear of rain.'

Sunday

Two days to go. Woke up feeling a bit … I don't know … tired.

After Sunday Club, Greg said, 'If I don't see you before marathon day, Danny, I hope you have a great run.'

'I'm going to have the best run,' I said. 'I'm going to be the fastest.'

'Well, I hope so, too,' Greg said. 'Because it's what you want.'

'There's no *hope* about it. I'll be the fastest. And that's how it's going to be.'

Tuesday 5am

I've been awake all night. At least, it feels like I've been awake all night. I've got a headache. And I'm hot. And I itch, too, and my eyes are sore.

I don't feel good.

I didn't feel good yesterday either.

This is bad.

Today's the day. Mini-marathon day. The day I get my name on the trophy.

10.30am

How?

11.30am

It's the holidays.

It's mini-marathon day.

I've been training for the last two weeks.

And I've got chickenpox. Apparently.

How?

11.35am

And come to think of it, WHY?

You knew how much I wanted to be fastest, Lord God! You knew I wanted this more than anything else in the whole wide world.

Why have You let this happen?

Why?

Later

Paul and Greg came to see me.

I said, 'Keep away. I'm covered in germs.'

Paul said, 'That's OK. I've had chickenpox.'

'Me, too,' said Greg.

'And if I was going to catch it again (which I'm not sure I can),' Paul added, 'I already would have done. You're infectious before the spots come out.'

'What,' I said, 'me especially?'

Paul said, 'No, people with chickenpox in general.'

'I didn't know that,' I said.

'Please don't be miserable, Danny,' Paul said. 'I mean, I know you feel ill, which is enough to make anyone miserable. And it's no fun being covered in spots. But don't be upset over the mini-marathon.'

'You don't understand,' I moaned. 'I wanted to do this SO much. It's all I've been thinking about. I thought this was the year I could start being a famous marathon runner. I wouldn't be famous straightaway obviously, but this would have been like the first step.'

'The first run,' Paul nodded.

'Exactly. The first proper run. And what I really don't get,' I went on, 'really, *really*, REALLY don't get, is that God knew how important this was to me. I talked to Him about it all the time. I asked Him to help me run better. Faster. And now … well, I just can't believe it. I'm *so* disappointed.'

'We know,' said Greg. 'We would be, too. I know you think we don't understand about being competitive, but we do. And we understand about disappointment. Look, Danny, I know there's probably nothing anyone can say that will make you feel better, but I'm going to say it anyway.

'The thing about God is He doesn't always stop us from being disappointed. Being a Christian doesn't mean that everything is always going to be fantastic. God doesn't promise that we'll *always* have a great time, just because we're friends with Him.

'But what He does promise is that, when things go wrong, which they will, and when we're disappointed, which we're bound to be sometimes – then He'll always be with us. He'll be right beside us going through whatever we're going through.

'We might not always get what we want, Danny,' Greg smiled, 'but we've *always* got God on our side.'

'And guess what?' grinned Paul. 'We've been on the internet, haven't we, Greg?'

'Yup,' said Greg.

'And there isn't another mini-marathon for a bit, but there is a cycle race coming up round Holly Hill.'

'Is there?' I said.

'Yup,' said Greg.

'And as I've got so good at cycling,' Paul went on, 'what with being your personal trainer and everything, and you're already really good at cycling – well, I thought we could enter.'

'I want to be a runner,' I said.

'I know that,' said Paul. 'And you *will* be. I'm your personal trainer. I'll make sure of it. But in the meantime, we could be world class cyclists and get our names on a world class cycling trophy.'

'World class?' I said, a bit doubtfully. 'In Holly Hill?'

'You could,' said Greg.

I thought for a moment. Then, 'Yeah,' I nodded. 'I guess we could. And then, maybe I could start to be a famous marathon runner next year.'

'Like I say, I'm your personal trainer,' said Paul. 'I'll make sure of it.'

Paul's Perfect Holiday at Home Day

Paul LOVES the first day of the school holidays. He can get out of bed when he wants; wear what he wants; eat what he wants (as long as it's in the cupboard); play the games he wants to on the computer; and read the books he wants (not what he *has* to read for homework).

But the BEST thing about the first day of the school holidays for Paul is that, because it's the FIRST day, it means that all the other holiday days are still to come!

What would be YOUR perfect holiday at home day?

- What time would you get up in the morning?

  _____

- What would be your favourite clothes to wear?

  In winter _____

  In summer _____

- What would be your perfect breakfast?

  _____

- What's the first thing you would do *after* breakfast?

  _____

- Would you want to spend the day on your own or with a friend?

  _____

- If you'd like to spend it with a friend, who would you choose?

  _____

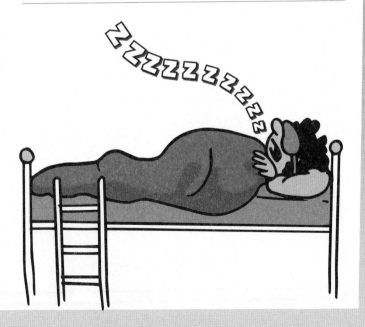

What if ...?

The Topz Gang have been wondering how it would feel to be able to go on holiday somewhere completely *out of this world* – like ... the moon!

Imagine that you're all packed, you're dressed in a spacesuit, your ticket is in your pocket and you're waiting to climb aboard the moon rocket ...

Now imagine what your hotel on the moon might be like when you get there ...

Draw a picture of it here:

There are different activities to do on your moon holiday, but you are only allowed to do ONE thing a day.

What would you choose (tick one for each day)?

Day 1
Moon-walking ☐

Moon-skateboarding ☐

Moon-tap-dancing ☐

Day 2
Moon-space-hopping ☐

Moon-roller-skating ☐

Moon-football ☐

Day 3
Moon-frisbee-throwing ☐

Moon-dry-swimming ☐
(Topz don't know what this is either, so it could be a good one to choose and find out!)

Moon-tenpin-bowling ☐

> I don't think a holiday on the moon should be called a 'moon holiday'. It should be called a 'mooliday'!

51

More Perfect Holiday at Home Fun

- Would you stay in or go out?

  _____

- If you went out, where would you go?

  _____

- What games would you like to play – computer games, board games, card games – and which ones?

  _____

- What favourite book would you like to curl up with?

  _____

- What TV shows would you watch?

  _____

- If there was nothing on TV that you wanted to watch, what DVDs would you choose?

  _____

John's Helpful Holidiary

Sunday

Mega project. Mega, MEGA project. Benny would say stonking. (In fact, I think he did.)

It's all Greg's idea. He announced it at Sunday Club this morning. He wants Sunday Clubbers to organise it with Friday night's Youth Clubbers – 'it' being a BIG church hall sale! That's what we're going to call it: The BIG Church Hall Sale.

No, we're not selling the church hall. We're going to make posters and 'spread the word', as Greg says, asking people to donate all the stuff in their houses that they don't want any more – clothes, ornaments, books, DVDs, jewellery, even furniture. Then it's all going to be sold off in the church hall, with the money raised going to the homeless shelter. It's such a cool idea! If we get some proper decent bits of furniture or jewellery, Greg says he'll run a mini-auction, too!

The sale's going to be in three weeks' time, which means we have three weeks to get together a pile of fantastic stuff to sell.

'That'll keep you busy in your school holidays,' Greg said. 'I want this to be big. And I mean BIG!'

We're having a Topz meeting in the morning. If we all work together, all seven of us, we reckon we'll manage to get loads of donations. We can start with our own houses.

I said to Mum, 'Do you really need all those flowerpots outside the back door? Imagine how much money The BIG Church Hall Sale could make if you sold them? And what about all that fancy soap in the bathroom? You never use it. You just say it looks pretty

53

and makes the room smell nice. Wouldn't it be great to sell it and raise money for the homeless shelter?'

I gave Mum a huge grin. She can never resist my huge grins.

Well, almost never.

Just on *some* days. Today being one of them.

'Raising money for the homeless shelter is a great idea, John,' she said, 'and I promise to turn out some things. But please leave my flowerpots and fancy soap alone. Thank you.'

9.30pm

Can't wait till tomorrow. We're having our Topz meeting here. We'll make the posters first of all so that we can put them up round Holly Hill as soon as possible. We're going to go knocking on people's doors, too, asking for donations. Greg says we can leave plastic sacks with people for them to fill, like the charity shops do. And he says he'll hire a van so that he can make special trips to collect everything.

I love it when Topz have something to do all together. Sarah will probably team up with Josie because that's what she nearly always does. So that means I get to team up with the boys, which is awesome – because the Topz boys' team is just bound to be topz (obviously) …

Is it tomorrow yet …?

Monday 1pm

Decided not to help with The BIG Church Hall Sale after all. It's stupid. Pointless. Why should I waste my time? There's more than enough Topz doing it without me as well.

Apparently.

1.30pm

I wish I never looked forward to anything. Not ever. The more you look forward to something, the worse it is when it turns out to be rubbish.

6pm

I was really excited about our Topz meeting this morning. *Really* excited about getting stuck into Greg's project. Being on the Topz boys' team.

But I guess that's the trouble with odd numbers. The odd one always gets left out. Sarah's pairing up with Josie, just like I knew she would. Which leaves five boys. And in the meeting, it turned out that four of them had already paired up with each other.

Leaving the fifth one on his own.

The fifth one being ME.

'Cos apparently Benny had been talking to Danny, and Paul had been talking to Dave, and by the time we had our Topz meeting, they'd already decided to work together. In pairs.

'Oh,' said Paul, when Benny said he and Danny were a team. 'That's funny because Dave and me, we've decided to be a team, too.'

'And Josie and me are going to be a team *obviously*,' Sarah said. She gave Josie one of those girly hug things. I mean *why*? Being in a team with someone does not mean you have to start hugging them.

'So …' I said. 'Who am I going to be in a team with?'

'Oh,' said Paul again. 'I dunno. I mean, Dave and I didn't know about Benny and Danny or Josie and Sarah, and we've kind of worked out our own plan for how we're going to do this. Erm … John, is there any chance you could join Danny and Benny?'

'Well, actually,' said Benny before I had a chance to say anything at all, 'Danny and I have worked out what we're going to do, too. We decided we'd just work in a twosome.'

'But,' I said, 'I thought that's why we were having this meeting. To decide what we're going to do and how we're going to do it.'

'I know,' said Benny, 'but when I was round at Danny's yesterday afternoon, we sort of sorted it out between us.'

'So did we,' said Paul. 'Dave and me. I suppose we thought maybe you and Sarah would –'

'No, you didn't!' I snapped. 'You thought, let's just do what *we* want and forget about John. After all, it's easier doing things in twos and John's number five. And five is two plus two with one left over!'

Benny shook his head. 'Erm … sorry, no, you've lost me.'

'No one wants to do Greg's project with me!' I yelled. 'Fine! 'Cos I wouldn't work with any of you now even if you asked me!'

After supper

Sarah said, 'You don't have to go all sulky with the boys. It's not *their* fault. They were just trying to get organised.'

'Yeah, by leaving me out,' I muttered.

'They didn't mean to leave you out,' Sarah said. 'You

know they didn't. It's all just got in a bit of a muddle. Anyway, they all said you could join their teams before they went home – and you said no.'

'Because they didn't ask me straightaway! It's not like they *want* me to work with them, is it? It's 'cos they suddenly felt bad when they realised they'd left me out!'

'But you wouldn't have to be all on your own anyway,' argued Sarah. 'You could get together with someone else from Sunday Club. Or from Youth Club.'

'But I'm a Topz!' I shouted. 'I wanted to do this with Topz!'

'Will you two please stop arguing,' groaned Mum. 'Otherwise I think I might put the pair of *you* up for sale to raise some money for the homeless shelter!'

In bed
I wish I wasn't on holiday.
   I wish I was back at school.
   And I hate school.

Tuesday evening
Saw Mrs Allbright this afternoon. She was just coming out of her front gate when I got back from a Gruff walk.

'I've just seen a poster for The BIG Church Hall Sale,' she said. 'It's your church that's holding that, isn't it?'

I nodded. 'Yup.'

'Well,' she smiled, 'I have a few things I'd be very happy to donate. A lovely chest of drawers and a small writing desk, and some little bits and pieces, too. The furniture ought to fetch something worthwhile, I'd have thought. Can I leave it to you to get everything collected?'

I didn't know what to say. I'm not helping with the

sale. But I didn't want to tell Mrs Allbright that. And the furniture sounded brilliant.

'Erm …' I mumbled.

'It says on the poster that things can be collected. That is right, isn't it? I mean, I live right next door to you, so I'll be very easy to find!' she chuckled.

'Yeah,' I said. 'OK, I'll tell Greg. Our youth leader. He's going to hire a van. I'll check with him when the collection day is.'

'It's in about two and a half weeks,' smiled Mrs Allbright. 'The date's on the poster. I seem to know more about it than you do!'

That's true. Mrs Allbright seems to know way more about it than I do.

But then I've decided not to help so why would I know anything?

Wednesday morning
Went to see Greg.

I said, 'I'm not helping with The BIG Church Hall Sale but our neighbour, Mrs Allbright, has some things to donate and they sound quite good. So I thought you'd like to know because they'll need collecting.'

Greg raised his eyebrows.

'Why aren't you helping?' he asked. 'You were really up for this last Sunday.'

'Yeah, well. Stuff happens.'

'What stuff?'

'Doesn't matter.'

'John …?'

I sighed. When Greg wants to know something, you sort of have to tell him.

'Topz wanted to work in pairs. Danny and Benny. Paul

58

and Dave. Josie and Sarah. Which leaves me. So I'm not doing it.'

Greg's raised eyebrows pulled themselves together in a frown. Greg has very expressive eyebrows, I've noticed.

'That doesn't sound like Topz,' he said. 'Topz wouldn't leave you out. Not on purpose. They're your best mates. Are you sure this isn't some sort of misunderstanding?'

I shrugged.

'Have you talked to them about it?'

'A bit,' I mumbled.

'And ...?'

I shrugged again.

'Mmm,' said Greg. 'Sort it out, Johnny. Like I say, Topz are your best mates. This all sounds like a big muddle to me.'

'That's what Sarah said.'

'You should listen to Sarah. She knows what she's talking about. Meantime,' Greg went on, 'I'm going to need a right-hand man.'

'A what?' I asked.

'A right-hand man. I need someone to make a list of all the addresses I'll have to go to so that I can collect donations. *And* I'll need someone to come with me on collection day to help me get things into the van.'

'Oh,' I said.

'You could be just the man I'm looking for.'

It was my turn to frown.

'What ... you want *me* to help you? You want *me* to be your right-hand man?'

'Certainly do,' said Greg. 'I've got a good-sized search party out there hunting for donations but I haven't got anyone to help with the pick-ups. So how about it?'

'Erm …'

'Please say yes. I really need your help with this, John.'

'Well … OK,' I said. 'I mean, yes. Cool. That'd be awesome.'

Wednesday evening

'I told you it was only a muddle,' said Sarah. 'No one meant to hurt your feelings, John.'

'I know,' I said. 'Well, I know that *now*.'

Then Sarah said, 'You do have a habit of overreacting, John,' and I said, '*You* can talk,' and Mum said, 'Please be quiet before you give me a headache.'

In bed

*Thank You, God. Greg says no matter how we feel – whether it's happy or sad, important or not important at all – to You we're all **priceless**. You have an amazing plan for each one of our lives and we have our own vital parts to play in all Your other plans. Even me.*

I've been feeling so small, God. So unimportant. But You've shown me that I do have a part to play – even in something like The BIG Church Hall Sale.

So, like I say, thank You, God. You've made me Greg's right-hand man.

Planet Puzzles

God created an amazing universe – including awesome Planet Earth, which He made sure had everything we needed to live. And then He gave it all to us to enjoy and to care for.

But how much do you know about our universe? Do the quiz and find out. (Tick the right answers.)

1. What is the sun?

☐ A planet ☐ A flying bonfire ☐ A star

2. There is a special force that holds us down on the earth. Is it …?

☐ Grip ☐ Gravity ☐ Gravy

3. Does the earth orbit (travel round) the moon?

☐ Yes ☐ No ☐ I'm still stuck on No. 2

4. If you were in space, would you be able to breathe oxygen the same way as you can on earth?

☐ Yes ☐ No ☐ I'm still stuck on No. 3

5. Which is the only planet in our solar system to have LOTS of water?

☐ The sun ☐ Earth ☐ Neptune

6. The earth travels round the sun in how many days?

☐ 10 ☐ 1 ☐ 365

7. Which is the smallest planet in our solar system?

☐ Mercury ☐ Mars ☐ Snickers

8. Which is the biggest planet in our solar system?

☐ Twix ☐ Jupiter ☐ Milky Way

9. Has anyone ever walked on the moon?

☐ Yes ☐ No

Answers on page 121

And did you know …?

The Bible says that God created the universe in six days, and on the seventh day, He had a rest. Rest days are important. God knows that we need them. So He's pleased when He sees us having a holiday!

62

Sarah's Rainy Day Quiz

Rainy days happen. They just do. But one of my favourite things to do when I can't go outside is to grab a groovy book and have a read. Sometimes I get so wrapped up in a story that hours can go by and I've hardly noticed. SO – here's my idea for a *fandabulous* rainy day quiz! How many book titles do you know? And who wrote the books ...?

Have a look at these famous book titles. Can you fill in the missing word or words in each one?

1. James and the _____

2. The Secret _____

3. The _____ Children _____

4. Alice's _____ in _____

5. _____ and the _____ Factory

6. Where the _____ Are

7. The _____ of Peter _____

8. The Wind _____ the _____

Answers on page 121

Did you guess them all? Now look at this list of authors. Can you match the right author to the right book? (Write the number of the book next to the name of the person you think wrote it. There may be more than one book by the same author.)

Beatrix Potter

E. Nesbit

Roald Dahl

Kenneth Grahame

Maurice Sendak

Frances Hodgson Burnett

Lewis Carroll

Answers on page 121

How many of these books have you read? Which one is your favourite? Write it down here – or if there's a book you like more than all of these, write its title (and the author if you know it) instead.

More Rainy Day Match Ups:
FLAGS

Every country in the world has its own flag. So, if people do a lot of travelling around the globe on holiday, they're likely to come across a lot of different flags.

Here are just a few (if you can find flag pictures on the internet, you'll see how colourful they are, too!):

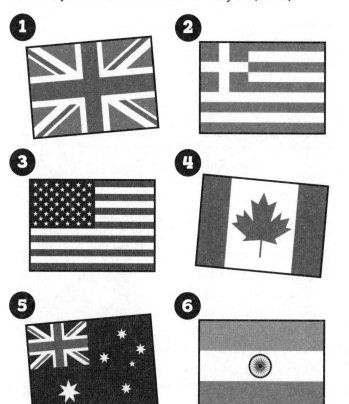

Now look at this list of countries. Can you match the right country with the right flag? (Write the number of the flag next to the country you think it represents.)

Australia _____

Greece _____

United Kingdom _____

India _____

Canada _____

USA _____

Answers on page 121

Funky Flag Facts

- Flags have been around since the seventeenth century.
- Colours on flags mean different things. Red usually means 'power'.
- In 1969, the astronaut, Neil Armstrong, erected the American flag on the moon when he landed there.
- World flags tend to be rectangular or square-shaped. The flag of Nepal, however, is shaped like this ➙

Gruff and Saucy's Pet-Sitting Holidiary

One Day

Saucy:

I heard them plotting. 'It's not "plotting", it's "planning",' Gruff says. But I heard them: Sarah and her mum talking to a lady who calls herself a 'pet sitter'.

'What's a pet sitter?' I hissed to Gruff when he came back from his walk with John.

'Erm … someone who sits on pets … maybe?' Gruff answered.

'Why would someone sit on pets?' I asked.

'It makes perfect sense if the pet is a horse,' Gruff replied.

'But Sarah doesn't have a horse. Neither does John. The only pets to be sat on in this house are you and me,' I said. 'So I really don't think that's it.'

'Why do you want to know what a pet sitter is anyway?' Gruff asked.

'Because,' I said, raising my back into a slight arch to show that I wasn't happy, 'there's one in our lounge. Talking to Sarah and her mum.'

'Interesting,' nodded Gruff.

We sat at the lounge door and listened.

After a few moments, Gruff said, 'Uh-huh. They're going on holiday. The pet sitter's coming in to look after us.'

'That can't be right,' I replied. 'Mrs Allbright next door always looks after us if they go on holiday these days.'

'Not this time,' said Gruff. 'Maybe Mrs Allbright's

going on holiday, too.'

Gruff did one of his deep ear-scratch things. Then he shook himself.

'Now, I wonder if there's any food anywhere … by any chance,' he murmured, and wandered into the kitchen.

I stayed by the lounge door. I kept listening.

That's when I heard the pet sitter say it.

That's when she said: 'It's really good of you to ask me to look after your pets. As I said on the phone, I've been doing dog walking for a while. But this is the first time I've done proper pet sitting. And the first time I'll have looked after a cat. I suppose I'm more of a dog person, really. I mean, I like cats, obviously, and I'm sure your little Saucy is gorgeous, Sarah. I think I'm just more used to dogs.'

I froze.

I suppose I'm more of a dog person?

Sarah was talking to a pet sitter who's more of a *dog* person!!

Well that's that. That is most definitely that.

It's not happening. I am not being *'pet sitted'* by a dog person!

Not not not not NOT.

Gruff:

Cats can be SO weird. I don't want John and his family to go away either. I don't understand why humans have this thing about 'needing a holiday'. They should just walk more. In parks (like John and me) and woods and along by rivers. I like walking through the shopping centre, too. The smells there can be out of this world! A *lot* of dogs walk through the shopping centre. Especially in wet weather.

Anyway, the family's going away so John's going with

them. Which is a bit not good, but at the same time, they've arranged for a pet sitter to come and stay while they're not here. So we'll be fed and fussed (not sat on – my mistake), and I'll be walked. Sounds hunky-dory to me.

But, oh no, that's not good enough for Saucy.

'They're plotting to leave me with a dog person,' she said.

I said, 'They're not "plotting", they're "planning". They've arranged for someone to look after us. Cool. I mean, I'll miss John, but I know he's coming back, and I'll also get to make a new friend.'

'A new friend who's a *dog* person,' Saucy hissed.

'And what's wrong with that?' I asked.

'But how would you feel if they were a *cat* person?'

'I dunno. They're not.'

'Well, I'm not happy. Our pet sitter's never even done pet sitting before.'

'Doesn't matter,' I yawned. Must be getting towards my nap time. 'The family wouldn't leave us with someone who wouldn't look after us properly. Besides, I quite like the idea of taking someone new for a walk. Be a bit like having a holiday myself.'

Saucy turned her back on me and stuck her tail in the air. I think she's sulking.

Two weeks later

Saucy:
Sarah's gone. She's gone with the whole family on their holiday.

I tried everything to stop her.

I wrapped myself around her legs all day yesterday so

69

that she could hardly move for tripping over me.

I kept sitting inside her suitcase to make it really hard for her to pack her clothes.

I even pretended to be off my food.

'Saucy knows,' I heard Sarah say to her mum. 'She knows we're going away and leaving her with someone who isn't Mrs Allbright.'

'She can't possibly know,' replied Sarah's mum.

'But she does,' insisted Sarah. 'She won't leave me alone. And she's not even eating.'

'She'd eat if she was hungry,' said Sarah's mum.

'Huh! That's all *you* know,' I thought. 'I am absolutely starving but I'm not eating. Not until I've made my point.'

'You don't have to worry,' Sarah said, as she lifted me out of her suitcase for about the fifteenth time. 'The pet sitter lady is very nice. And she'll look after you very well. And I'm sure she's very good with cats, even though you're the first cat she's looked after. And you needn't worry about your snuggles. I have told her that you are a cat who needs someone to snuggle up to.'

'But how can a dog person know how to give a cat a snuggle?' I wanted to ask. Of course I couldn't. So I meowed and meowed. If I sounded *really* pitiful, surely Sarah and the family wouldn't go on holiday.

But they did.

They have.

They're gone.

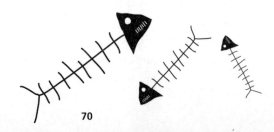

Three days later

Gruff:

This pet sitter is the *best*! She doesn't just give me walks – she runs with me! She's a proper jogger! I mean, when she said she was a dog person, she didn't say she was a super-fit, 'joggy' person, too! She wears all the right gear and everything. I am turning into a mega sporty dog. When John gets back from his holiday, he won't be able to keep up with me!

Saucy said, 'You don't seem to be missing your John at all.'

I said, 'I am! I love my John. But seriously, our pet sitter jogs! She *jogs*!'

Another day later

Saucy:

Dogs can be so shallow.

Gruff's excited – all the time – because the pet sitter jogs.

I said, 'Well, good for you. I'm glad one of us is being properly looked after.'

Gruff said, 'What d'you mean? You're being properly looked after, too.'

'I am *not*,' I said. 'I am missing my snuggles.'

'Sorry for being the dog to point this out,' Gruff said, 'but isn't that because you're ignoring the person who can give you snuggles while Sarah's not here? Our pet sitter in other words.'

'I am not ignoring her.'

71

'You *are*, though. You've ignored her since she got here.'

'Well, it's not my fault I don't like jogging,' I said.

Gruff said, 'John told me this thing before he went away. He said he hoped I'd get on well with our pet sitter – even be good friends with her. Then, if he ever went away on holiday again, he'd know that he could leave me with someone I like and get on well with. Then John said: "Do you know how to make a good friend, Gruff? You join in with them – and be a good friend to *them*."

'I wondered how John knew this,' Gruff continued. 'Then he said: "You see, that's what Jesus did. He didn't make friends with people by staying away from them. Or ignoring them. He made friends with people by joining in. By saying, 'Here I am. I'll be your Friend.'"'

'What's your point?' I asked – pointedly.

'Maybe,' Gruff said, 'our pet sitter's afraid to give you snuggles because she thinks you don't like her. Maybe if you started to be *her* friend, she'd start to be *yours*.'

I narrowed my eyes.

'Did I say I wanted to be her friend?' I hissed.

'No,' said Gruff. 'But I know you do.'

Two days after that

Saucy:
They'll be home tomorrow. My Sarah and her family. I'm glad. It'll be cosy being able to snuggle up to my Sarah again. Although I must say that our pet sitter is pretty good at snuggling, too.

I tried it, you see. Not just because of what Gruff said. I mean, since when did cats ever listen to dogs? No.

I just tried it because I thought … I might as well just try it. Being her friend.

Our pet sitter had just been out jogging with Gruff. She was in the kitchen putting the kettle on for a cup of tea. So I did it. I wrapped myself around her legs. I looked up and I meowed. And our pet sitter looked down with the BIGGEST smile on her face.

'Hello, gorgeous!' she said. 'Have you finally got used to me?'

Very slowly, she crouched down. Very gently, she reached out a finger to tickle my ear.

'I thought you didn't like me,' she smiled. 'I'm so glad to find you do. Because I like you. I really do.'

I rubbed the side of my head into her knees. Her smile grew bigger and bigger.

'Does this mean we're friends?' she said.

'Well …' I thought to myself. 'Well, yes. I think it probably does.'

'Thank you, little cat,' beamed our pet sitter. 'D'you know what I've realised since meeting you? I'm still a dog person. But now I know I'm a *cat* person, too.'

Radio Star! (1)

Dave LOVES listening to the radio – ever since he received one as a present for his last birthday. And he has a secret. He wants to be a radio star!

So, in the school holidays, Dave practises being a DJ (which stands for 'disc jockey' in case you didn't know – meaning someone who plays discs) in his bedroom. He works out the music he's going to play (his playlist), and then he writes himself a script so that he can natter away to his pretend listeners, just like a proper DJ!

In fact, Dave's practising right now! Let's take a sneaky peek …

Hello, hello! Thanks for tuning in. Great to have your company! I'm going to be playing some stonking songs to help you through the day. And I don't know about you, but I really feel like having an adventure! Disappearing off on one of those activity-type holidays would be ace. Canoeing, rock-climbing, abseiling … sounds like my kind of fun. How about you? What would be your idea of an adventure? Why not give me a call and you can tell the world all about it! Anyway, enough of that. I think it's time for some music …

DJ-you!

Having a job that means you spend the day chatting to people and playing music sounds VERY cool! Do you fancy being the star of your very own radio show, like Dave? Of course you do!!

So let's get started!

The first thing your radio show needs is some FANTASTIC **music**. Use the space below to make a list of your favourite songs. If you have them on CD, that's brilliant, because you can play them in between talking to your listeners. If not, no problem – you can sing them instead!

Favourite songs to play (or sing):

_____

_____

_____

_____

_____

_____

Radio Star! (2)

Now it's time to start thinking about your **script**. There's no need to write it out completely – you're not making up a radio play. You just need a good idea of some different topics you could talk about. Perhaps, like Dave, you could make 'holidays' the theme of your show. You could chat about places you've been and things you've done on holiday. And maybe you could do a count down of the TOPZ TEN craziest things that have happened to you outside school term time.

Have a think! If you don't want to talk about holidays, there must be lots of other things you could chat about between playing music on your show – for example, pets, favourite books or TV programmes, weirdest fashions …

Write down the topics you're going to talk about here:

_____

_____

_____

_____

_____

_____

Topz Talk

Very often, DJs will invite a special celebrity guest onto their show and **interview** them. The guest might be an actor, a singer, an author, a sports personality, or someone else who is famous for what they do.

Wouldn't it be great to invite the Topz Gang onto your show and interview them?! See if you can think of some really interesting questions you could ask. (Obviously when you come to do the interview on your radio show, as well as *asking* the questions, you'll have to *answer* them as if you were a member of Topz. But you can base your answers on what you know about the Gang.)

Scribble down some questions for your interview here and get ready for some Topz talk!

_____

_____

_____

_____

_____

_____

Radio Star! (3)

Music, chat, interviews! What an awesome way to spend a holiday day!

But did you know that lots of radio stations also use **advertisements** like you find on TV? There might be adverts for shops or other businesses – even for schools!

Here's one advert Dave came up with to broadcast on his radio show:

The sun is shining. The sky is blue. What a perfect day to get out on your bicycle! But, what's this? Oh, no! The last thing you want is a flat tyre! Still, not to worry. Just get yourself along to Dave's Bicycle Repair Shop. Dave knows all there is to know about bikes. He'll have you up and cycling again in a jiffy.

Dave's Bicycle Repair Shop. The only place to go with a broken bicycle.

Your turn!

Do you get the idea? Dave's Bicycle Repair Shop isn't a real business, of course. Dave's made it up – although sometimes he thinks he'd like to run a shop like that when he grows up – when he's not being a DJ!

Now it's your turn to think of something you could advertise on your radio show – real or made up. When you have a good idea, use this page to write yourself a short script for your advert. Then you can read it out between playing music on your show. If you have more than one idea for an advert, grab some extra paper to write down more scripts!

_____

_____

_____

_____

_____

Radio Star! (4)

SO – you've worked out your playlist; you know what your chat is going to be about; you've planned your interview; you even have an advert lined up! You're **almost there!** Your radio show is just about ready to go!

Just one final thing. When you watch a programme on TV, it will always have a theme tune – special music for that particular show that plays at the beginning and the end. In a similar way, at the start of a radio show, a DJ will usually have his or her own **jingle**. The jingle will be his or her name, and perhaps the name of the radio show, sung to a short, simple tune.

Dave calls his radio show: 'Daytime with Dave' – and he's made up a little tune for those words which he sings at the beginning of his show, and sometimes after he's played a song, too.

What will you call your radio show? Will it be your name on its own? Or will you use your name as part of the show title? When you've come up with something, write it here:

_____

Now invent a catchy little tune to sing it to – and you've got your jingle!

Ready ... Steady ... Broadcast!

The time has come! You might want to have a little rehearsal first, but when you feel ready to go, you can either set yourself up with a radio studio in your bedroom and 'broadcast' your show from there like Dave does. OR, if you're feeling brave, you can make a space in your lounge and invite your family and friends to come in and watch you 'broadcast' your show live!

When you've done one show, you might have so many more ideas that you want to plan and broadcast a brand-new one – maybe even a whole series of them!

Happy DJ-ing!

And if you'd like some TOPZ facts to throw into your chat mix, here are some all about radio ...

- A man called Nikola Tesla is believed to have invented the radio as long ago as 1892, although he never actually built one.
- The very first radio factory was opened around 1899 in Chelmsford in Essex by Guglielmo Marconi.
- The BBC (British Broadcasting Corporation) was formed on 18 October 1922.
- An American called Walter Winchell first came up with the term 'disc jockey' (DJ).
- The first disc jockey in the world EVER was Ray Newby, a 16-year-old student who lived in California, USA.

Sarah's Stranger Holidiary

Thursday

It's *so* not fair! I've said it before and I'll say it again –

IT'S *SO* NOT FAIR!!

This is *my* holiday, too, you know. So why do I have to spend it with some STRANGER in the house?

No, I'm not talking about John (although boys don't come much stranger than him). I'm talking about that *other* boy. The one we've never met before. The one who's staying here for the next three nights. The one who means we can't be PRIVATE in our own house!

It's all Mrs Parker's fault. Can't wait till she's not my class teacher any more. She used to teach in this school up in Cumbria and she came up with this *brilliant* (according to her) idea of getting her class in Holly Hill to link up with a class in the same year from the Cumbria school.

We all had to exchange photos and 'getting to know you' information, and then – *then* – Mrs Parker said we could email each other. See if we could build some 'proper friendships'!

'Who knows?' she said. 'You might all make some new best friends.'

I mean, honestly!

I said to Josie, 'Why would we want to make *new* best friends? We already have friends. And anyway, you're my *best* friend, Josie, so I don't need to make another one, do I? Especially not one who lives 4,000 miles away, or however far it is to Cumbria from here. I think it's stupid.'

Josie said, 'It might be quite fun to have friends in another school in another part of the country. It'll sort of be like going to two schools at the same time.'

'Yes, but *emailing* them?' I argued. 'Emailing kids we don't even know? Kids we're never even going to get to meet?'

'We might meet them,' Josie replied. 'Mrs Parker might arrange a school trip.'

'Ugh,' I said. 'Well, I'm not emailing anyone. No one at all.'

And I didn't.

Trouble is, John did.

He's been emailing this boy called Arran. Then he had to go and ask Mum if Arran could come to stay. And Mum had to go and say – YES.

I said to Josie, 'If John's having some STRANGER to stay with him, then *you* can come and stay with me at the same time. Otherwise, I know what'll happen. It'll be all boys, boys, boys, and I'll be totally left out.'

But then Josie said, 'I'm really sorry, Sarah, but that's when I'm going to stay with Gabby.'

I said, 'What?? But you can't! I *really* need you to be here, Josie. And you saw Gabby not that long ago. Can't you just not?'

'Sorry,' Josie said again.

'Well, can't Gabby come to stay here instead?'

'No,' Josie said. 'It's all been arranged.'

Why is it arrangements can be made just like that, but it seems so much harder to *un*make them?

So, like I say. Here I am in my own house with a STRANGER. A STRANGER who's a boy. A STRANGER who's staying with John and not me. Who's doing stuff with John and not me. Who's friends with John and not me.

Huh. Happy holidays, Sarah.

IT'S *SO* NOT FAIR!!

Friday
Mum said, 'You're quiet.'

I said, 'I'm eating my breakfast.'

Mum said, 'Doesn't normally stop you talking.'

I said, 'Well, this isn't a normal day, is it? There's a STRANGER in the house.'

'Arran's not a stranger,' Mum said. 'He's a friend of John's. And a very nice friend. I've had a few lovely chats to his mum on the phone. I think this school link-up thing is such a good idea of Mrs Parker's.'

There you are, you see. Everyone in the whole world seems to think it's a good idea, except me. Everyone.

Even Josie.

That's why I'm quiet.

Mum said, 'Why don't you do something with the boys this morning?'

'I don't want to,' I said. 'They won't want to do anything *I* want to do, and I won't want to do anything *they* want to do. And that's it.'

'So, you're just going to spend all day sulking, are you?'

'I am *not* sulking!'

'Well, it looks like it to me. The thing is, Sarah, if you'd chosen to email someone from the Cumbria school the way John did, you could have had someone to stay as well. Then you'd both have had a friend here and you wouldn't be sulking.'

'I'm *not* sulking.'

'You're carrying on as if they're deliberately leaving you out,' Mum said. 'And they're not. You're leaving *yourself* out – which is probably making Arran feel quite uncomfortable and is actually rather selfish.'

Huh! Selfish!

I'm not the one who's being selfish here. John was selfish in the first place for emailing someone in Cumbria when I thought it was a stupid idea. Mum was selfish for agreeing that Arran could come to stay. And perhaps the most selfish person of all is Josie – for going away to stay with Gabby when I need her here with me!

Me, selfish? I don't think so!

'Everything isn't always all about you, Sarah,' Mum said. 'Arran's come here for a little break. What he needs just now is for people to be kind. The least you can do is try to make it a bit nice for him.'

And who's making *my* holiday nice for *me*?

That's what *I'd* like to know.

Sunday (really early)

Yesterday, I read two whole books. *Two whole books.*

That's the sort of thing you do when you're left on your own. You read a lot. Well, that's the sort of thing *I* do anyway. And I had time to read *two whole books.* That's how long I was left by myself. (Not by Saucy, of course. Saucy hardly ever leaves me on my own. Even when I want her to.)

At least it's Sunday which means I get my house back. My PRIVATE-NESS back. Arran's going home.

11.30am

Oh, no. Mum's right. I'm so selfish.

I have been *so* selfish.

3.30pm

Arran's gone.

We just got back from taking him to the station.

I've said sorry to him about a million times. I hope he knows I mean it.

And I've said sorry to God.

Arran didn't go for a walk this morning with John and Gruff. I heard him upstairs. I thought it must be because it was raining. But that wasn't it at all.

You know when someone's crying. Even if they're crying silently, which some people do, you just know.

I just knew when I walked past John's bedroom door. It wasn't shut completely. And I just knew that Arran was crying.

I knocked.

No answer.

I knocked again.

'Arran? Are you OK? Can I come in?'

He didn't say I could, but I went in anyway.

'Why are you crying?' I asked. 'What's the matter? Has John done something? Is that why you've not gone for a walk?'

Arran shook his head.

'Are you sure?'

'Yes,' he muttered. Very quietly. More like a whisper, really. He looked so, so sad.

'Then, what's wrong?'

Arran didn't answer, but all of a sudden I answered the question myself.

In my head.

It wasn't John at all, was it? It was me! I'd been so horrible and unfriendly! Here was Arran 4,000 miles away from home and I hadn't been nice to him at all!

'Oh, no!' I gasped. 'It's me, isn't it? I've upset you! I'm so sorry. I didn't mean anything – really! I just … I just like to know people before they come to stay. I'm just quite … well, you know … private.'

Arran shook his head again.

'It's not you,' he mumbled. 'I'm used to people not liking me.'

'What?' I gulped. 'I never said I didn't like you. I *do*! I mean, I would I'm sure – if I got to know you.'

'No, you wouldn't.'

'Why wouldn't I? John likes you.'

Arran shrugged.

I sat down next to him on the bed.

'Look, I'm sorry. I'm really, really sorry,' I said.

'It's fine,' said Arran. He wiped his eyes with the back of his hand. 'Like I say, it's not you.'

'Then … what is it?'

'I don't want to go home!' he blurted out. Suddenly. Just like that. 'Mum and Dad – well, they're not going to be Mum and Dad much longer. They're breaking up. Dad won't be there when I get home. Mum arranged for me to come and stay with you so that he could move out. She thought it wouldn't be so bad for me if I wasn't there to see it happening.'

I stared. I swallowed.

I didn't know what to say.

Oh, please, God, I prayed, *please help me know what to say.*

'Arran, I'm so sorry!' I began. 'I didn't know. I'm so, so sorry.'

'I didn't *want* you to know. Or John. Your mum knows. Your mum and your dad, but that's all. I thought if you

two didn't know, everything might seem … normal …
and then it might not happen.'

'But it has. Hasn't it?'

Arran didn't answer. And when he nodded, he hardly
moved his head. He pulled his mobile out of his pocket,
clicked onto a text and held the phone out to me.

*Hope you've had a great few days, Arran. I've been
thinking of you all the time. I'm so sorry about all of
this. But just remember, it's not your fault. It's nothing
you've done. And Mum and I love you to bits. Absolute
bits. I'm going to see you next weekend. We'll go and
do boy stuff, OK? I do love you, Arran. Dad xx*

I read the words slowly.

Then, 'That's what you've got to remember,' I said.
'Your mum and dad love you. This isn't your fault. And
your mum and dad will always be your mum and dad.
Even if they're living in different places.'

Arran took the phone back.

'You should keep that text,' I said. 'For ever and ever.
And you should read it every day.'

9.30pm
*Dear God, I'm so sorry I've been so selfish. I'm often
selfish, aren't I? I think about me first, instead of
about other people. I want to get my own way all the
time. I think about what I can get out of everyone and
everything – instead of what I can give.*

Mum told me to be kind to Arran, and I didn't listen. Please help me to change, God. Help me to love other people – even the ones I don't know very well. Help me to put them first. Like Mum said, everything isn't about me. The last few days should have been all about Arran.

So this is my prayer for Arran, God. He's home now. And his life's going to feel really different. Not good different, either. Sad different. Please stay close to him. Please help him to know that he does have friends – in Cumbria, even though he seems to think no one likes him, and now in Holly Hill, too. Help John and me to be really good about remembering to email him – just so he never feels all on his own. And please, please make sure Arran never forgets that his mum and dad love him.

Maybe one day soon, God, you'll help John and me to tell Arran about You. Then he'll know that You love him, too. That You'll never leave him on his own.

Be Arran's best Friend, please, God. Thank You.

Do You Know Who's Who in the Bible?

See how well you know who's who and who did what in the Bible. Try this TOPZ holiday quiz! (Tick the right answers)

1. What was the name of the very first man (Old Testament)?

☐ Adrian   ☐ Aslan   ☐ Adam

2. What was Abraham's wife called (Old Testament)?

☐ Susan   ☐ Sarah   ☐ Shona

3. Which disciple did Jesus call 'The Rock' (New Testament)?

☐ Percy   ☐ Peter   ☐ Paddy

4. Who was Samuel's mother (Old Testament)?

☐ Hambel   ☐ Harriet   ☐ Hannah

5. Who led God's special people, the Israelites, through the Red Sea (Old Testament)?

☐ Moses   ☐ Michael   ☐ Mowgli

6. Jesus brought Mary and Martha's brother back to life! What was his name (New Testament)?

☐ Lionel   ☐ Lenny   ☐ Lazarus

7. Who ran away from God and was swallowed by a big fish (Old Testament)?

☐ Jonty   ☐ Jonah   ☐ Johnny

8. Which very small man had to climb a tree so that he could see Jesus over the heads of a crowd of people (New Testament)?

☐ Zacchaeus   ☐ Zachary   ☐ Zechariah

9. Who was Isaac's wife (Old Testament)?

☐ Rowena   ☐ Rebecca   ☐ Rosalind

10. Who killed a giant man called Goliath (Old Testament)?

☐ Derek   ☐ Dermot   ☐ David

Answers on page 122

Do you know who's who?
How many did you get right?

Even More Rainy Day
Match Ups: Countries

Here is a list of countries – and on the opposite page is a list of facts about them. Can you match the right country with the right fact? (Write the number of the fact next to its country.)

Russia

Scotland

Thailand

Ireland

Egypt

Spain

Greece

England

Brazil

Wales

Mexico

China

1. This country's population is the biggest in the world.

2. This country holds a national holiday on St Patrick's Day.

3. Between this country and France are some mountains called the Pyrenees.

4. Spanish is the main language spoken in this country (clue: not Spain!).

5. The money in this country is called 'rubles'.

6. The River Severn is the longest river in this country.

7. This country is known as 'the land of song'.

8. The highest mountain in this country is called Ben Nevis.

9. This country's national symbol is the elephant.

10. Corfu is an island belonging to this country.

11. The Nile, the longest river in the world, flows through this country.

12. The most popular sport in this country is football.

Answers on page 122 How many did you get right?

And Even MORE Rainy Day Match Ups: FOOD

Guess which member of the Topz Gang came up with the idea for this match up quiz … It's the one who enjoys eating … and eating … and eating some more … (If you think it's Benny, you're absolutely right!)

For this match up, you need to match the food with the country. Here's a list of different tummy fillers, and on the opposite page are the countries we usually associate with them. (Write the number of the food next to the right country.)

1. Goulash
2. Sushi
3. Roast beef and Yorkshire pudding
4. Cheeseburgers
5. Irish stew (bit of a giveaway!)
6. Pizza
7. Paella
8. Haggis
9. Borscht (vegetable soup usually with beetroot)
10. Pain au chocolat (pronounced pan-o-shockola)

Ireland

France

Russia

Hungary

Scotland

USA

Japan

Spain

England

Italy

Answers on page 122

Now you've done the quiz, are you as hungry as I am? What do you fancy eating right now?

GGGGRRRRRROOOWL

Paul's Painful Holidiary

Tuesday, 2pm

'What are you doing?' Mum asked.

'Isn't it obvious?' I answered.

'Are you writing in your diary?' Mum asked.

'Uh, yes, obviously,' I answered.

'No, *not* obviously,' said Mum. 'Why have you even got your diary with you?'

'I picked it up on the way out.'

'I thought you were in pain.'

'I was. I am.'

'But not enough pain to stop you thinking, "Ooh, I know what I must do! I must grab my diary!"'

'The thing is, Mum,' I explained as patiently as I could, 'you know what these hospital Accident and Emergency departments are like. You can be stuck in them for ages. Just sitting. Waiting. Like when Danny broke his arm. He was there for hours. And hours and hours. He told me. And I get bored, Mum, I really do. I get bored very quickly. So I thought, I'm not taking any chances, and I grabbed my diary.'

'Mmm,' muttered Mum.

She's reading a magazine now. There were only two on the table in front of us. One's about motorbikes and the other's about gardens. Mum's reading the garden one.

2.15pm

Just tried to move my foot. Ugh. That hurt. That *really* hurt. A funny sort of noise came out of my mouth. Half a squeak and half a moan. Mum looked at me.

'What's the matter?'

96

'I just tried to move my foot,' I winced.

'Why?' Mum sighed.

'It was an experiment. I thought it might not be painful anymore.'

'Of course it's going to be painful,' said Mum. 'Your ankle's at least twice the size it should be. You just need to keep the whole thing still until we've seen the doctor.'

'Right,' I nodded. 'Good.'

It's hard though. Keeping a part of your body still. The second you know you mustn't move it, moving it is all you want to do.

2.30pm

Mum's up.

'That coffee machine's out of order,' she said.

'How d'you know that?' I asked.

'There's a sign on it that says "out of order".'

'Is there?' I asked. I peered.

'Yes, right there,' said Mum. She pointed. 'I think you need to clean your glasses.'

'Don't mention my glasses,' I replied.

Mum shook her head. 'I'm going to find another machine. Now sit still and don't move your foot.'

2.35pm

You see, it's because of my glasses that we're here. In Accident and Emergency. Mum would disagree. She'd say the whole reason we're in Accident and Emergency is because I'm not careful enough about where I leave them. If I was careful, Mum says, I wouldn't forget where I've put them if I take them off for something like having a shower. Or, as happened this morning, if I get something in my eye and have to take them off to try to get it out. (The something, that is, not my eye.)

Whatever the something was, I couldn't find it. Sadly, when I went to put my glasses back on, I couldn't find them either.

'Mum!' I called. 'Mum, have you seen my glasses?'

No answer.

'Mum!' I tried again. 'I only took them off a few minutes ago and they've vanished. Seriously, they're nowhere.'

Again, no answer. So I thought I'd go downstairs to find her.

That was the mistake, right there. OK, so I can barely see two centimetres in front of my face when I'm glasses-less, but I reckoned I'd be fine. I'd hold onto the banister with one hand and stretch out the other one to touch the wall and balance myself. And I'd move really, *really* slowly. What could go wrong?

As it turned out, everything.

Three steps down and somehow or other I hurtled forwards, bounced (yes, really), thudded and landed in a heap at the bottom of the staircase.

Mum shot out of the kitchen.

'What are you doing?' she asked.

'Looking for you,' I whimpered.

'Where are your glasses?' she demanded.

'Dunno,' I groaned. 'That's why I was looking for you.'

Shortly afterwards my ankle did this. Ballooning, Mum calls it. I wish she wouldn't. It makes me anxious. As if all of a sudden it might go pop.

2.40pm

A nurse has just come out to the waiting

room and called someone else through. At least, I think she's a nurse. She's wearing one of those smart-looking and incredibly clean uniforms, so I think she must be. And she has a clipboard. Clipboards make you look smart and incredibly clean, too. And clever.

2.45pm
Mum's not back yet. How far do you have to go in this hospital to find a cup of coffee?

Evening
I LOVE days like today. Not so much the falling downstairs and spraining my ankle part. (Yes, when I finally got to see her, the doctor said it *was* only a sprain. Bit disappointing really. With the size it had 'ballooned' to, I thought I must at least have broken it in six places.)

No, what I love about days like today is that they whizz off in weirdly unexpected directions.

When I woke up this morning, I thought, Yay! I'm on holiday!

Little did I realise I was soon to fall downstairs.

And when I sat in the Accident and Emergency waiting room doing the waiting bit, little did I realise who would come and sit in the seat opposite to me.

His name's Frankie.

He stared at my ballooned up ankle. He didn't speak. He just stared.

Soon, a tall man came and sat next to him. He was cuddling a little girl and holding a big pad of cotton wool to her head. He saw me looking.

'Fell over, didn't you, poppet?' he said. 'Gave her head a proper crack.'

'Ow,' I murmured, as sympathetically as I could.

99

'You look as though you've been in the wars yourself,' said the man. He nodded towards my ankle.

'Fell, too,' I said. 'Down the stairs.'

'Sorry,' replied the man.

'Thanks,' I smiled.

'It's the waiting, isn't it?' the man went on. 'If you could just turn up, see the doctor and go, then you could get on with your day.'

'Yes,' I said.

Mum still wasn't back. I wished she'd hurry up.

'Do you live in Holly Hill?' the man asked.

'Erm … yes,' I answered.

'So do we now,' said the man. 'Moved in last Wednesday. Come down from Bradford. Have you heard of Bradford?'

I had so, 'Yes,' I said.

'This little one's called Cate,' the man added, giving Cate a squeeze. 'And my boy here, he's Frankie.'

'Hi,' I said.

Frankie didn't answer.

'Bit of a shy one,' his dad said. 'Say hello at least, Frankie.'

Frankie didn't.

Mum came back, with a mug of coffee in one hand and a mug of hot chocolate in the other.

'Who'd have thought it would be so hard to find a working coffee machine?' she grumbled, passing me the hot chocolate. 'Gave up in the end and went all the way to the top floor to the restaurant. The lady serving said they don't do take away and I said, "Well, I'm sorry, but my son's down in Accident and Emergency with a ballooning ankle and your machines all seem to be out of order, and I *need* a cup of coffee!"'

Mum sat down and sipped her drink.

No one spoke. So I thought perhaps I should say something.

'Mum, this is Cate and, erm, Frankie. And their dad. And they've just moved to Holly Hill from, erm ...'

'Bradford,' said the man helpfully.

'Bradford?' answered Mum. 'That's a long way away. And what's your little one done?'

'Banged her head.' It was weird. The man and I said that at exactly the same time.

'So you'll be starting at Holly Hill Primary after the holidays, then, Frankie,' smiled Mum.

Frankie didn't answer.

'Yes,' nodded his dad. 'He's a bit nervous about it, to be honest.'

'Nothing to be nervous about,' said Mum. 'It's a lovely school. How old are you? You must be about the same age as Paul. You might even be in the same class.'

'Who's class is it you'll be in, Frankie?' asked Frankie's dad.

'Mrs Parker's,' Frankie mumbled. He still hadn't taken his eyes off my ballooned up ankle.

I started to say, 'I'm in Mrs Parker's class,' but Mum got in first.

'There you are, you see, Paul's in Mrs Parker's class,' she beamed. It's the happiest I'd seen her look all day. Well, since before I fell downstairs.

Again, Frankie didn't speak.

'She's very nice,' I said. 'Mrs Parker. And our class is pretty cool. I'll have to introduce you to my friends. Although they're all a bit crackers. Are you OK with crackers?'

For the first time, Frankie raised his eyes, very slowly from my gigantic ankle, and looked at me.

'How come you fell downstairs?' he mumbled.

'I lost my glasses,' I shrugged. 'Well, I didn't exactly lose them. I just couldn't find them.'

Frankie looked as if he didn't quite follow.

'What I'm trying to say is,' I went on, '*you* try doing stairs when you can hardly see two centimetres in front of your face. It's an accident waiting to happen. Seriously.'

Mum raised her eyes. 'And you call your friends crackers,' she muttered.

9.30pm

Frankie's coming over tomorrow. His dad's dropping him off. I've invited all the Gang, too. Partly I want them all to see my bandage and the massive balloony-ness of my ankle, but partly I want Frankie to meet them.

Frankie *is* shy. Just like his dad said. He's *really* shy and he's been dreading the holidays being over and having to start at a new school.

I told him I understood. I can't understand completely, obviously, because Holly Hill Primary is the only school I've ever been to, and me and Topz, we've known each other forever. But I said I understood it must be hard, starting a whole new life in a whole new place where you know a whole new nobody.

'Only, you don't know nobody now, Frankie,' I grinned, right before Mum pushed me out of Accident and Emergency to the car in a really funky wheelchair. Which, sadly, we didn't get to keep. 'You know *me*. And after tomorrow, you'll know all of Topz. So when term starts, school won't be nearly so scary.'

And Frankie smiled.

10pm

Dad says I'm a nifty hobbler. In other words, I'm learning how to hobble niftily.

Cool.

Also cool is that Dad has always said God can bring good even out of painful situations. I mean, falling down the stairs was *mega* painful, and I do now have an ankle of maximum balloony-ness, which means no footie or bike riding for a bit. (And no helping with the hoovering either, which is a plus!)

But if that hadn't happened, I probably wouldn't have met Frankie. And if I hadn't met Frankie, he might have spent the rest of the holidays worried sick about starting a new school. Instead of which, by the time he walks into the classroom on his first day, he's already going to have friends. Topz and me.

'You see?' Dad said when he came up to say goodnight. 'There's always a bigger picture. Bigger than any of us can see. But God sees it. And His good plans for us are HUGE.'

John's Jolly Journey Guide

Going on a journey can be exciting –
especially if you're heading off for
somewhere really cool for a holiday.
But long journeys can get a bit boring,
too. That's why I've put together
this guide to help you have the most
fandabulous fun you can possibly get out
of travelling. You're going to love it!

1. Time to rhyme! How many words can you think of
that will rhyme with each of the following:

Hat	Hot	Book
Sun	Key	Vole
House	Green	Fill

2. Try to make up a rhyming poem using some of the
words you've come up with.

3. Count up to 100 in twos, then fives, then tens. When
you've done it, see if you can count to 200 in the
same ways.

4. How many words can you think of that begin with
the same letter as your first name?

5. Now how many words can you think of that begin
with the same letter as your best friend's first name?
(If your best friend's first name begins with the same
letter as yours, pick one of the Topz Gang whose name
starts with a different letter, and use theirs instead.)

6. Which words are normally paired up with the following:

Fish and _____

In and _____

Hot and _____

Black and _____

Up and _____

Bubble and _____

On and _____

Thunder and _____

Answers on page 122

7. People take their dogs for walks, just like I take my dog, Gruff. But what would be your idea of the weirdest animals in the world to take for a walk? Try to come up with ten different and very weird animals.

8. Sticking with weird, what would be your TOPZ ten weirdest places to go on holiday?

9. Still sticking with weird, pick one of your TOPZ ten weirdest places. Now think – what would be your weirdest form of transport for getting there?

Hope you're not still bored!

Danny's Capital City Quiz

If your holidays take you to a different country, it might be quite useful to know which is the capital city of the country you're staying in. Here are a few countries people like to visit. Do you know the capital cities for each one? Write them in the right spaces. I've given you some clues (in case you need them) – the first *capital* letter of each *capital* city...

Ireland, D

Germany, B

Sweden, S

Israel, J

Scotland, E

Spain, M

Mexico, M   C

Russia, M

Wales, C

USA, W   D.

Answers on pages 122–123

What a lot of lovely places there are to visit! And that's just a teeny handful of them!

Here's another list – this time of different ways people might travel to the places they want to visit.

Bus	Ferry	Aeroplane
Private car	Ship	Bicycle
Helicopter	Coach	Taxi
On foot	Motorbike	Minibus

See if you can find them all in the word search.

```
U  F  L  G  I  G  Z  O  R  T  P  N  Q  O  B
D  E  B  U  E  N  A  L  P  O  R  E  A  S  J
Z  R  B  U  U  H  F  U  R  V  R  V  W  I  R
M  R  R  S  W  E  H  M  A  I  X  A  T  M  K
F  Y  A  M  H  L  E  N  R  Q  N  Z  X  A  K
J  M  C  O  B  I  C  Y  C  L  E  H  I  J  O
F  H  E  T  Y  C  P  W  G  P  S  U  B  U  V
S  A  T  O  L  O  G  R  S  U  B  I  N  I  M
C  B  A  R  X  P  C  T  V  N  X  W  L  B  M
I  T  V  B  U  T  G  X  Q  A  T  G  Q  Q  V
D  B  I  I  X  E  Q  C  T  O  I  P  F  G  W
A  C  R  K  H  R  A  T  O  E  S  T  I  F  V
A  T  P  E  U  P  T  F  R  A  W  Q  O  H  Z
E  N  L  M  G  B  N  U  Y  M  C  U  D  B  S
E  K  I  B  R  O  T  O  M  I  I  H  M  O  W
```

Answer on page 123

Benny's Brilliant Holidiary

Thursday 9.30am

I've got it! I'VE GOT IT!

I know what I need to do to make this holiday BRILLIANT! To turn it into the one I'll remember FOREVER!

I need a challenge! I need to come up with and COMPLETE A CHALLENGE!!

So simple! Yesss!!

10am

OK, maybe not so simple.

Can't think of a challenge.

6.30pm

I asked Dad, 'If you were going to set yourself a challenge, what would it be?'

Dad said, 'I've always rather fancied sailing round the world single-handedly.'

'Really?' I said. 'I never knew that.'

'Maybe that's because you've never asked,' Dad said.

I nodded. 'But,' I said, 'what if you were going to set yourself a challenge that was a bit easier?'

'A challenge should never be easy,' Dad said. 'Otherwise it wouldn't be a challenge.'

'No, I don't mean "easy",' I answered. 'I mean, easier than sailing round the world.'

Dad looked thoughtful. 'Tricky,' he said. 'Erm … I suppose I've always liked the idea of learning a different language. Mandarin, for example. Now that would be a challenge.'

'But … wouldn't that take a really long time?'

'Probably,' Dad replied. 'Especially for me. I've always been terrible at learning languages. Mind you, sailing round the world would take a long time, too.'

'Yes,' I said. 'Yes, I suppose it would … So, if you weren't going to sail around the world or learn Mandarin – what other challenge could you do? Something that might not take quite so long.'

'Well,' Dad said, 'I suppose growing a cactus plant from a seed might be a good one.'

'Can you grow cactus plants from seeds?' I asked.

'No idea,' said Dad.

I was beginning to think that Dad wasn't the best person to help me. So I went to find Mum.

'Mum,' I said, 'if you were going to set yourself a challenge, what would you pick?'

'That's easy,' said Mum. 'I'd learn a musical instrument. I've always wanted to learn a musical instrument.'

All my life my mum has just been 'my mum'.

I realise now that she is in fact a 'mum genius'.

Of course! Learning a musical instrument! A brilliant challenge to make for a brilliant school holiday!

7pm
Fine.

So Mum may be a genius. She is also totally not prepared to help me in my brilliant challenge plan.

I said, 'This school holiday, I'm going to learn to play the keyboard.'

'That's interesting,' Mum said. 'How do you intend to do that?'

'Easy,' I said. 'You can find lessons on how to play instruments on the internet.'

'I'm sure you can,' said Mum. 'But aren't you forgetting something?'

'Am I?' I asked.

Mum said, 'In order to learn to play the keyboard, Benny, you sort of need to have *a keyboard*. And the last time I looked, we haven't.'

'But we could *buy* one!' I answered. Sometimes grown-ups can be put off by the teeniest of problems. 'And when we've bought one, you can learn to play it, too, Mum. There you are you see – one keyboard – two challenges! Stonking, huh?'

Mum looked at me.

'When you say "we",' she said, 'I assume you mean your dad and me? You mean your dad and I could buy a keyboard?'

'Well, yeah,' I said. 'If I have to save up my pocket money, I'll never get to learn how to play it this holiday.'

'Benny,' Mum said, 'your dad and I don't have the money just to go and buy a keyboard. So I'm sorry, but no.'

'But, Mum –'

'No!'

Fine.

FINE.

9pm

'Who do you know who plays a musical instrument?' asked Mum.

'Not me, apparently,' I grunted.

'Yes,' said Mum in her patient voice, 'but who do you know who does?'

I shrugged. 'Josie's learning to play the violin. Don't

110

know why. *I* wouldn't want to learn to play the violin.'

'Who else?'

'Why?'

'Who else do you know, Benny?'

'Erm ... Danny plays the guitar.'

Mum raised her eyebrows.

'What?' I said.

Then I got it.

'Danny plays the guitar!' I yelled. 'So ... maybe I could ask Danny if he could teach me to play the guitar, too. Using *his* guitar!'

'And there you have it,' said Mum. 'One holiday challenge coming right up.'

Like I said before – 'mum genius'.

Friday morning

PLAY GUITAR CHALLENGE – DAY ONE

Danny's coming round in a minute. He's bringing his guitar.

I've been warming up my fingers. I want them to be all ready to play when he gets here.

First I soaked them in warm water in the bathroom basin. Then I opened and closed my fists lots of times, stretching my fingers right out. And I've just been pretending to play keyboard on my desk, doing plenty of finger waggling.

I think they're ready.

Let's play guitar.

Friday afternoon

Hmm.

As Dad says, I suppose a challenge wouldn't be a challenge if it was easy. And playing the guitar is *not* going to be easy.

Danny tried to teach me to play a chord. I tried *very* hard. But I found it *very* difficult.

I said, 'Maybe I have the wrong shaped fingers.'

'You don't have the wrong shaped fingers,' said Danny. 'You just have to learn how to hold them in the right position.'

I think Danny could be wrong. I'm sure my fingers would be stonking at playing keyboard. After all they work brilliantly when I play my desk. Not convinced they're the right shape for playing guitar, though.

Still Friday afternoon

And the tips of my fingers are *really* sore! Danny says that's normal because they have to get used to pressing down on the guitar strings.

So playing the guitar is painful … Who knew?

Saturday morning

PLAY GUITAR CHALLENGE – DAY TWO

OK. I can do this.
If it hurts – it hurts.
If Danny can play guitar – so can I.
Bring it on.

Night

So ... I got what I wanted. I wanted this to be a school holiday I'd remember for ever.

And it will be.

It'll be the one I'll never forget. Never ever.

The school holiday when I broke Danny's guitar.

Sunday morning. Early. Very early. Not properly light early

Some things happen so quickly, it's hard to work out what happened at all.

I'd learned to play a chord on Danny's guitar. The chord of G. It was an exciting moment. The ends of my fingers hurt like mad and my whole hand ached from trying to stretch them into the right position. But I'd got it. At last.

And I was really happy.

So was Danny.

I put the guitar down on the bed so that I could do a victory dance. Victory dances are important. Danny and I always do them when we're playing football and we score a goal.

So I was doing my victory dance. And Danny was laughing. I know he was laughing because that made my dance even crazier.

Then, suddenly – I jumped up onto the bed.

I don't know why.

I wasn't really thinking.

I just jumped up onto the bed – and put my foot straight through the guitar.

7am

I can't get the noise out of my head. The noise my foot made when it crunched through the wood.

It was horrible.

It made me feel sick.

I still feel sick now.

7.10am

Danny's face was the worst thing.

He went white and his mouth actually dropped open.

He almost looked as if I'd put my foot through *him*.

Sunday night

He's never going to forgive me. Danny.

He said, 'I'll never forgive you for this, Benny, *never!* I should have known you'd break my guitar! I should never have brought it round to your flat! I should never let you touch *any* of my things *ever*! Well, I never will again. And I will never forgive you for this, Benny, *never!!*'

I wanted to point out that he'd already said that last bit. But then I thought, perhaps he meant to. Saying it twice means much more definitely that he'll never forgive me than saying it once.

When Danny left with his broken guitar, he didn't even say goodbye to Mum.

Danny always says goodbye to Mum.

In bed

Dad asked, 'Have you been crying?'

'No,' I said. 'Why would I have been crying?'

Dad answered, 'Maybe because one of your best friends is angry with you?'

'He's not just angry with me, Dad,' I said. 'He's never going to forgive me.'

'He says that at the moment,' Dad smiled. 'But he will.'

'No,' I said, 'I don't think so.'

'What you did,' said Dad, 'was a bit silly.'

'Putting my foot through Danny's guitar? I think it was more than a "bit silly", Dad.'

'But you didn't mean to,' Dad went on. 'You were doing a victory dance in a confined space. Probably not the most sensible thing in the world, but it was an accident. And deep down Danny knows that.'

'You reckon?'

'Yes, I reckon.'

I shook my head.

'Makes you think about God though, doesn't it?' Dad said.

'Does it?' I answered.

'Well, it makes *me* think about God,' Dad said. 'Look at all the things people do. The horrible, mean, selfish, nasty, cruel, unkind things people do. To each other and to the planet. And a lot of what they do isn't because of victory dances in confined spaces. It isn't accidental. It's done on purpose. It's done to hurt.

'But God still wants to forgive them. God still wants to forgive *us*. And when we ask Him to, He will. He does. Which is actually pretty incredible, isn't it?'

I nodded. 'But Danny's not God, is he? And he hates me.'

'Forgiving each other isn't easy, Benny. God knows that. He always forgives us when we ask Him to, but there must be times when He doesn't find it easy either. Especially when we do the same things wrong, over and over again.' Dad smiled at me and picked up my Bible. He flipped the pages to the book of Matthew in the New Testament – chapter 6, and he pointed to verse 12.

'When Jesus taught His disciples how to pray,' Dad said, 'He told them to say to God, "Forgive us the wrong things we have done, as we forgive the wrongs that others have done to us."'

He put the Bible down, but left it open at that page.

'Ask God to help Danny forgive you, Benny,' Dad said. 'Ask Him tonight. After all, He wants Danny to forgive you as much as you do.'

Monday morning

I rang Danny's front door bell.

Danny opened the door.

I said, 'If your guitar can't be fixed, which I know it probably can't be, then Dad will go with you next weekend to buy a new one.'

Danny didn't smile or anything. He just looked at me.

'I'm going to save up my pocket money so that I can pay him back. Actually Dad's just going to give me less pocket money each week until he's got the money back. It was my idea. After all, it was my foot that made the hole.'

Danny didn't speak.

'OK,' I said. 'Just thought I'd tell you.'

I turned to go.

'Benny,' Danny said.

'Yeah?'

'I know you didn't mean to do it.'

'Good,' I said. 'Because I didn't. I really didn't.'

I started to walk away.

'I was just, erm …' Danny said.

'What?'

'I was just playing a game on the computer. D'you …
wanna play, too?'

'Which game?'

'That car one.'

I nodded.

'I like the car one.'

'And me.'

'It's a good game, the car one.'

'Yeah,' Danny said. 'It's a great game. A stonking
game. But … well … it's just … it's just better with two.'

Put Your 'Stamp' On Your Holiday!

Whether you spend your school holidays at home or whether you go away, it's good to let your friends know what you're up to. Why not send them a postcard telling them what you're doing? Don't forget to put a stamp on each one before you post them!

Some stamps have interesting pictures on them. If you could design your very own stamp, what would it look like? Draw it here:

Answers

FROM HOLIDAY TREATS
Page 8
Word search solution

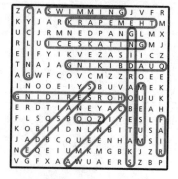

FROM BEACH HUT BARMINESS – SPOT THE DIFFERENCE!
Page 22
The odd beach hut out is d.

FROM MAKING JOURNEYS
Page 23
Manchester 1 hour
Iceland 3 hours
Egypt 5 hours
New York 7/8 hours
Singapore 13 hours

FROM BIBLE TRAVELLERS
Page 35
1 Mary and Joseph
2 They travelled from Nazareth
3 They travelled to Bethlehem
4 They had to go to Bethlehem to be counted in a census
5 Wise men

FROM JOSIE'S RAINY DAY QUIZ
Pages 36–37
Eiffel Tower: France
Nelson's Column: England
Taj Mahal: India
Statue of Liberty: USA
Leaning Tower of Pisa: Italy
Giza Pyramid and the Great Sphinx: Egypt
Sydney Opera House: Australia
Big Ben: England

FROM WHAT'S IN YOUR SUITCASE?

Page 38

Word search solution

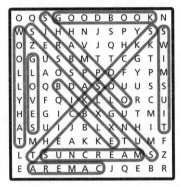

FROM PLANET PUZZLES

Pages 61–62

1 A star
2 Gravity
3 No
4 No
5 Earth
6 365
7 Mercury
8 Jupiter
9 Yes

FROM SARAH'S RAINY DAY QUIZ

Page 63

1 James and the Giant Peach
2 The Secret Garden
3 The Railway Children
4 Alice's Adventures in Wonderland
5 Charlie and the Chocolate Factory
6 Where the Wild Things Are
7 The Tale of Peter Rabbit
8 The Wind in the Willows

Page 64

Beatrix Potter: 7
E. Nesbit: 3
Roald Dahl: 1 and 5
Kenneth Grahame: 8
Maurice Sendak: 6
Frances Hodgson Burnett: 2
Lewis Carroll: 4

FROM MORE RAINY DAY MATCH UPS: FLAGS

Pages 65–66

Australia: 5
Greece: 2
United Kingdom: 1
India: 6
Canada: 4
USA: 3

FROM DO YOU KNOW WHO'S WHO IN THE BIBLE?

Pages 90–91

1 Adam
2 Sarah
3 Peter
4 Hannah
5 Moses
6 Lazarus
7 Jonah
8 Zacchaeus
9 Rebecca
10 David

FROM EVEN MORE RAINY DAY MATCH UPS: COUNTRIES

Pages 92–93

Russia: 5
Scotland: 8
Thailand: 9
Ireland: 2
Egypt: 11
Spain: 3
Greece: 10
England: 6
Brazil: 12
Wales: 7
Mexico: 4
China: 1

FROM AND EVEN MORE RAINY DAY MATCH UPS: FOOD

Pages 94–95

Ireland: 5
France: 10
Russia: 9
Hungary: 1
Scotland: 8
USA: 4
Japan: 2
Spain: 7
England: 3
Italy: 6

FROM JOHN'S JOLLY JOURNEY GUIDE

Page 105

Fish and chips
In and out
Hot and cold
Black and white
Up and down
Bubble and squeak
On and off
Thunder and lightning

FROM DANNY'S CAPITAL CITY QUIZ

Page 106

Ireland: Dublin
Germany: Berlin
Sweden: Stockholm

Israel: Jerusalem
Scotland: Edinburgh
Spain: Madrid
Mexico: Mexico City
Russia: Moscow
Wales: Cardiff
USA: Washington, D.C.

ALSO FROM DANNY'S
CAPITAL CITY QUIZ
Page 107
Word search solution

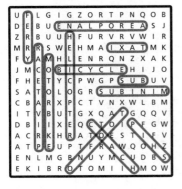

Topz is a colourful daily devotional just for you

In each issue the Topz Gang teach you biblical truths trough word games, puzzles, riddles, cartoons, competitions, simple prayers and daily Bible readings.

Available as an annual subscription or as single issues.

For current prices and to order go to
www.cwr.org.uk/topzeveryday call 01252 784700
or visit a Christian bookshop.

Discovering more about yourself and God

These *Topz Secret Diaries* will help you discover more about yourself and God. Includes questions and quizzes, engaging puzzles, word searches, doodles, lists to write and more.

Boys Only – Stuff about me

Fancy yourself as a footballer? Spaceship designer? Could you run your own TV channel – and, if so, what would you show? And how well do you REALLY know yourself – and God? Find all this (and much more) inside!

ISBN: 978-1-85345-596-4

Just for Girls – Special things about me

Ever dreamt of writing your own mag? Giving your friends a makeover? Designing your own dream bedroom? And how well do you REALLY know yourself – and God? Find all this (and much more) inside!

ISBN: 978-1-85345-597-1

For current prices and to order go to
www.cwr.org.uk/topzbooks call 01252 784700
or visit a Christian bookshop.

Meet each of the Topz Gang in their very own diary

Dave's Dizzy Doodles
You can always talk to God
ISBN: 978-1-85345-552-0

Gruff & Saucy's Topzy-Turvy Tales
Know God's help every day
ISBN: 978-1-85345-553-7

Danny's Daring Days
Confidently step out in faith
ISBN: 978-1-85345-502-5

John's Jam-Packed Jottings
Become a stronger person
ISBN: 978-1-85345-503-2

Paul's Potty Pages
Keep your friendships strong
ISBN: 978-1-85345-456-1

Josie's Jazzy Journal
You can show God's love to others
ISBN: 978-1-85345-457-8

Benny's Barmy Bits
Christians needn't be boring
ISBN: 978-1-85345-431-8

Sarah's Secret Scribblings
You are special to God
ISBN: 978-1-85345-432-5

For current prices and to order go to **www.cwr.org.uk/topzbooks**
call 01252 784700 or visit a Christian bookshop.

TOPZ SECRET STORIES

The *Topz Secret Stories* are full of fun and they also help you to discover things about yourself and God. The Dixons Gang present problems and opportunities to the Topz Gang.

Danny and the Runaway
ISBN: 978-1-85345-991-7

The Cloudgate Mystery
ISBN: 978-1-85345-992-4

One Too Many for Benny
ISBN: 978-1-85345-915-3

Pantomime Pandemonium
ISBN: 978-1-85345-916-0

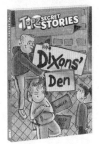

Dixons' Den
ISBN: 978-1-85345-690-9

Dixons and the Wolf
ISBN: 978-1-85345-691-6